THE REVOLT

and

28 MORE ORIGINAL

UWHARRIE GHOST STORIES

THE REVOLT

and

28 More Original

UWHARRIE

Ghost Stories

Fred T. Morgan

BANDIT BOOKS

Winston-Salem, North Carolina

Printed in the United States of America

Library of Congress Catalog Card Number 2004101546

ISBN 1-878177-15-X

Bandit Books, Inc.
P.O. Box 11721
Winston-Salem, NC 27116-1721
(336) 785-7417

Distributed by John F. Blair, Publisher
(800) 222-9796
www.blairpub.com

Author's photograph courtesy of Brooks Barnhardt

Title page artwork by Morgan Starnes

Original artwork by Patricia Storms, www.patriciastorms.cjb.net

Cover design by Holly Smith, bookskins.net

TABLE OF CONTENTS

INTRODUCTION

For many years I have advocated elevating our ghosts at least to the level of a natural resource, comparable to air, water, soil, minerals, wildlife, plant life, timber, ecosystems, and scenic grandeur. But I haven't made much headway. I am not a strong enough advocate.

What we need is an advocacy group or organization. Call it something like SPUG (Society for Preserving and Utilizing Ghosts). Its main job will be lobbying for ghosts and promoting ghosts—in every conceivable way and location.

For much too long we have neglected our ghosts. Technological sophistication is pushing them toward the endangered species list. Already some of the older ones have faded beyond resurrection. What a loss to our heritage. We are all diminished by the loss of one such spirited performer. I think the remaining ghosts, the survivors, the perpetuals, the newly arriving ghosts, are ready (for the most part) to cooperate in a massive, nationwide drive to identify, recognize, profile, enhance, and utilize every ghost in America—perhaps even to the point of re-locating some of them.

Is it not intriguing to contemplate re-locating a friendly ghost to the proximity of your town? One that will perform on a regular scheduled basis? Think of all the tourist—related business this will generate.

Re-locating a ghost involves some interesting logistics. You won't find many such services advertised in the yellow pages or on the Internet. Personally, I know of one or two such ghosts here in the Uwharries that might be persuaded to cooperate in such exploitation. However, their demand for amenities might be difficult to meet. But I will not reveal any more details about them. Nor will I serve in a semi-technical advisory capacity, or as a negotiator, in such an undertaking. Unless, of course, the price is right.

I believe our ghosts deserve more respect, more consideration, more acceptance, more dignity. From my experience in the Uwharries, I believe that the ghostly realm in America is a frontier breakthrough ready to happen. Then ghosts will be liberated from murkiness and myth. They will be understood, accepted and "howdy-ed" to as any other race or entity. And the benefit mankind will get from them might be incalculable.

There is plenty of room on the gigantic tapestry of American folklore for our country's ghosts to parade into their rightful prominence. I can almost see them—hear them—coming. Can't you?

If any of the ghosts in this book, or in earlier ones, strike you as good candidates for re-location and positive utilization, talk with your Chamber of Commerce, visitor's center, or facsimile. They can help make SPUG a reality. Perhaps you can volunteer. It's time to materialize some spook wheels and get them rolling in this direction.

Fred T. Morgan
Albemarle, North Carolina
December, 2003

THE SIKES SISTERS

Well into the wee hours one half-moon-lit night, Skeedaddle Holmes got scared out of his wits while riding his pore-ribbed mule, Ol' Maggie, bareback through one section of the Uwharries, following a night of intense carousing. The alcoholic aspect of his carousing probably contributed to the intensity of his fright and his subsequent verbalizing about it.

Maggie spooked and abruptly reared way up on her hind legs, snorting and whinnying and causing the unsuspecting Skeedaddle to tumble backward to the ground. While the tumble didn't break any bones, it sprained his shoulder, an ailment he complained about for the rest of his life. However, the sprained shoulder did not interfere with his headlong plunge out of the woods. When he looked at the spectacle for a few seconds, his eyes bulging, a scream and convulsion a-borning in his stomach, he scratched off like lubricated lightning, almost blazing a new trail through the woods. He never knew which direction he ran—just away from the ghost.

In fact his bulldozing path through the woods, traceable for many years because of the beaten down brush and saplings, earned him a nickname. Before the experience he was known as Skeever Holmes. After the experience and his ever-exaggerated versions of it, folks started calling him Skeedaddle Holmes.

No question about it, he skeedaddled all right.

What Skeedaddle saw has not been experienced by many people. They say it takes luck, fate, a proper mentality and personality, psychic ability, and a combination of other circumstances to gain an audience with these ghosts.

What Skeedaddle saw were ghostly animals. A parade of them. A street full of them, a circus full, an endless, thick line of them. It looked like a long, transparent tunnel full of ghostly animals, each one animated and recognizable as it glided before his eyes for a few seconds, then disappeared.

What kind of animals were in this ghostly parade?

"Ever kind there's ever been in the Uwharries," Skeedaddle is alleged to have said. "And then a lot more. You think I'm lying, but I swear, it looked like tigers and lions, elephants and monkeys, and camels and hippopotamuses. Even big long snakes. Mixed in with all the regular ones we see around here. All serious and peaceful. Not violent a-tall. None of 'em looked like they wanted to hurt anybody.

"Crazy, crazy. I know it sounds crazy. But I saw it!

"Another thing. Nobody believes this, but I saw it with my own eyes. They saluted! However best they could, they saluted. Just like the old military salute." Here Skeedaddle snapped his feet together, stiffened up straight, and jerked his extended palm over his right eye to demonstrate. "Everyone of 'em. They all did it. With their paw, their hoof, their tail, trunk, whatever. They saluted, I'm telling you.

"What were they saluting? It weren't me, I know that. So, you tell me. What were they saluting?"

The answer to Skeedaddle's question goes back to the dimmest reaches of Uwharrie folklore. Back to the Sikes sisters. Old maid sisters, Sally and Soonie Sikes were ancient, wrinkled, tall and thin, wearing long dresses and sun bonnets which hid most of their faces. They lived in a tumbledown shack at the edge of the big woods with their domestic animals, and tended their garden vegetables, herbs, and flowers. They didn't own the big woods. In fact, nobody knows if they owned the premises they occupied. But their gateway location was the most accessible path into the big woods for hunters after game. Most all hunters stopped by and chatted with the Sikes sisters before they entered the big woods. Some formally asked their permission to hunt. Others brought token gifts—sugar, coffee, matches, oil for their lamps and lanterns.

The big woods held a fabulous amount of wild game. Any hunter could go therein and quickly bag his limit of squirrel, rabbit, quail, turkey, and deer, along with coon, possum and foxes. Several streams with deep lakes provided abundant fish, frogs, and turtles, with muskrats, mink, and beaver for trapping. Also the woods offered the best in wild fruits—grapes, nuts, berries, and more. While other forests had all this, no other location could match the quantity and quality of the big woods.

The Sikes sisters were the key to successful hunting, fishing, trapping, and foraging in the big woods. All hunters and gatherers learned this sooner or later. If hunters tried to slip in without permission or contact with the sisters, they had no luck. They would see no game, catch no fish, find no fruits or nuts. Even if they did see game, they missed their target. Or their guns misfired or jammed. Fishermen and gatherers might well have stayed home, because they came away empty handed.

This led to some angry people and bitter recriminations. Some people called them witches and questioned their right and ability to control the big woods and all life therein. But the Sikes sisters paid them no mind. They went about their business, treating all visitors fairly and firmly. Everyone agreed—the Sikes sisters did control the big woods and everything inside. And they did it for scores of years, for generations, some people even said for hundreds of years. The sisters didn't appear to age or change like normal people.

Poor people, the underprivileged, or those facing a crisis got a better deal in the big woods when they made their circumstances known to the sisters. And some benefited without explaining their plight. The sisters knew without any verbal communication. These needy people always took home surplus, enough to sell for cash. But the pompous, the dishonest, the pretenders, even if they got into the woods, met with misfortune which kept them from coming back.

Rarely, if ever, did the sisters go into the big woods themselves, but they knew the terrain intimately. Frequently they told the hunters and gatherers the best place to go, describing the location in detail and warning them of hazards. If a prospector wanted to pan for gold, they directed him to the best place. Firewood gatherers were permitted to cut around the edges of the big woods. But no logging or timbering within. The area remained a sanctuary for generations.

Late in life and a sober man for years, Skeedaddle tried to explain it.

"They communicated with the wild animals, that's how they did it," he said. "Don't ask me how, I dunno, but that's how it was done. That's the way they controlled the population and density. Animals, fish, fruits, they knew all about them every minute. If hunters tried to sneak in, the sisters told the animals to remain still, quiet and out of sight. They had some sort of psychic power to make bullets go astray and guns jam.

"Sally and Soonie had no education. They never went to school, no special training. Yet they were the best wildlife managers anywhere, even though they did it remotely. Curators, game wardens, wildlife refuge operators, veterinarians, foresters, environmentalists—they did it all instinctively and they did it as good as it's ever been done to this day in this big woods world. True conservationists, true wildlife protectors. I'll bet they've never been equaled. Never will be. I'll bet nobody, and I mean nobody, could ever develop a greater rapport with animals than those two old ladies. They left us a legacy and a heritage. Maybe they set the foundation for our Uwharrie National Forest and wilderness area today."

He paused, reflected a moment, then continued:

"We ought to honor those ladies, perpetuate their memory some way. Yes, they ought to be honored for all they did."

Skeedaddle didn't know about it back then, but that's what the animal ghosts are doing–paying tribute to the Sikes sisters as saints and saviors in the animal world.

Progress inevitably decimated the big woods. Roads, houses, farms, and industry pushed through the area, displacing most of the animals. The creeks evaporated. Timber companies clearcut most of the woods.

Nobody knows what happened to the Sikes sisters, not even when or where they died or were buried. Apparently there is no record of any forebears or descendants.

Speculation is that they or their ghosts still roam the Uwharries, monitoring and protecting the animals, bringing misfortune upon those who mistreat them.

And those animals in the ghostly parade that are foreign to the locality?

Sympathizers.

In the ghostly realm, distance is no problem, so the ghosts of animals native to Africa or Siberia or anywhere else instantaneously can participate in this periodic parade of tribute.

A more recent witness of this parade of ghostly animals describes it much as did Skeedaddle. He saw animals foreign to the Uwharries, even dinosaurs. They were animated, peaceful, and recognizable. They saluted. Every one of them. He said they flowed along in a tunnel, sort of like on a TV weather screen when the jet stream from Canada loops down to the southern USA, then back up the East Coast. Saluting as they descended, the ghostly animals hit the bottom of the loop, then disappeared as they went back up.

Folks say you have a better chance of seeing these ghosts if you are a dedicated animal lover and go into the vastness of the Uwharries to meditate, perhaps to pay tribute to the memory of the Sikes sisters.

But be sure your intentions are positive.

OL' SIMON

When we left town and moved to the country in the edge of the Uwharries, my young son, Freddie, and I developed a leisure time activity which we practiced for years. In every direction from our property, we explored all the fields and woods and pastures, never suspecting that we would ever run into anything related to a ghost.

But we did.

In all seasons we rambled through wood and field, stopping frequently to closely examine anything interesting or anything that caught our eye. And there were many. We learned a lot about wildlife, plant life, rocks, soil, insects, snakes, birds, wetlands, creeks, springs, barns, crumbling old homesites, and family graveyards. We found Indian artifacts, grotesque tree and rock formations, gemstones, a little gold, hollow trees, squirrel nests, fox dens, deer rubs, grapevines, berry patches, nut trees, shagbark hickories, herbs, miniature waterfalls, pine knots, and walking-stick saplings.

But our most prized discovery was the old sawmill.

In a secluded part of the woods the old sawmill, which once turned big trees into lumber, had been abandoned to the elements. And the elements had been rough on it. It must have been decades since the machinery was last used. Small trees had grown up in and around it. A blanket of honeysuckles covered one end. Its sawdust pile had settled into the brush and mixed with the leaves and pine needles. Most of the woodstock chassis, the wooden frame, and other wooden parts had rotted away. Only the metal parts remained and they were tarnished with rust and greenish layers of corrosion. Everything sagged or leaned crookedly out of place.

Fascinated by the old sawmill, Freddie and I started visiting it regularly. A strange camaraderie kept pulling us there and keeping us there. It welcomed us. We could feel psychic vibrations. It appeared to develop a personality and appreciate our attention. Then it began to cooperate and prostrate itself for our convenience as we began our salvage operations.

7

We removed manageable pieces of the metal and took them home
with us as souvenirs. Stuff like bar braces, pieces of track, lengths of
chain, small pulley wheels, nuts and bolts, a hand lever. But the piece
I wanted most proved the most difficult to remove. It was the big saw
blade, which sliced through the logs lengthwise, converting them to
rough lumber. Three feet in diameter, an eighth of an inch thick, the
saw had sunk almost halfway into the ground litter. Years of rust had
frozen the round-shouldered nut in place on the end of the shaft, locking
the saw in position. We used a pipe wrench, but it wouldn't budge.
Then I began sloshing Liquid Wrench solution on it and banging hard
on the nut with a metal hammer, hoping vibrations would help loosen
it.

One day I tried an extra long handled wrench with an extension
persuader. Still no luck. I dropped the tools in frustration, walked off
and kicked in the dry leaves. Moments later, something made me turn
around and look back. The pipe wrench was back in place on the rusty
nut, its long handle positioned in the opposite direction. I put the
extension in place and gave a massive jerk. The nut broke loose. I had
been trying to loosen it the wrong way.

Elated, we unscrewed it, pried off the saw and brought it home in
our pickup truck. I had an ideal display space for it, a genuine smokehouse, the most prominent outbuilding around our farm home. The
walls of this picturesque weather-blackened building have become a
depository for country memorabilia. The old saw fitted ideally into the
gallery. I fixed a place and leaned the saw against the wall outside the
door, placing a brick under the bottom teeth to keep the heavy saw from
sinking into the ground. I considered wire brushing, sanding, and
re-finishing the old saw to make it more presentable, but somehow I
never got around to it. So the rust keeps on rusting and the corrosion
keeps on accumulating. And the old saw stands there to this day,
occasional bird droppings adding whitish exclamation marks on its
rustic face.

A year or two passed before I began to notice the ghostly light
bobbing at night in the wooded hillsides along Byrd Road.

Byrd Road is less than two miles long, so it isn't hard to spot the
ghostly light when it's out and active. Of course, you can't see it every
night. Just some nights. Usually in the winter time when less leaves and
foliage give better visibility into the woodlands. The south side of Byrd
Road presents a series of hills and hollers, woods and thickets, ideal for
deer and, apparently, for spirits too, for this is the lair of the ghost light.

I began asking questions, talking to neighbors, natives, and the community's elderly. If I lived within hollering distance of a real live ghost, I wanted to know more about him. It took a while, but I finally pieced together the story of ol' Simon.

Ancient and mostly decrepit the first time anyone can remember seeing him, Simon stood tall and rawboned, blocky face almost hidden by white beard and whiskers, wide, thick-lipped mouth, fiercely bright eyes, huge hands and feet, elbows and knees that always poked out of his clothing. Hot weather, he didn't wear much clothing. Cold weather saw him wrapped, almost mummy-like, in discarded quilts and blankets with special wrappings for his head and feet. If you had anything to throw away, Simon was a grateful recipient. He gardened a little bit, foraged for nuts and wild fruits, trapped a few rabbits and squirrels for meat, hauled spring water from half-a-mile away on his homemade wheelbarrow, and rummaged around in trash piles along the road.

Folks said he was illiterate. No one knew anything about his early life, his origin, occupation, family, or age. He communicated with gestures, grunts, and short words. Visitors were few. Mail was unheard of.

Simon lived in a rickety shack on a knoll in sight of the main road. Maintaining the tumbledown shack took most of his spare time. A conglomerate of poles, posts, wire, cable, slabs, crooked boards and timber, braces, cardboard and linoleum, it leaned and swayed in a windstorm. On top, rusty tin weighted down by rocks kept some of the rain out. He slept on a pile of rags and horse blankets in one corner. Near the center of the dirt floor, a sunken hole overflowed with wood ashes from countless fires used for cooking and warmth. Smoke and fumes easily escaped through holes in the walls, eaves, and roof. Occasionally a pet dog or cat occupied the shack with him. Someone said that he could talk to and tame birds. Others said he hummed a lot, a sort of chant-like monologue, which no one ever identified.

To earn a little money, Simon worked now and then for a few hours at a sawmill back over the hill from his shack. The sawyer gave him slabs and a few boards, which he dragged or rolled haphazardly home on his wheelbarrow. He utilized them to re-enforce his shack or for firewood. But offbearing the slabs and heavy green lumber was hard work, much too strenuous for aged and senile Simon. He could only work an hour or two at a time.

One day a newspaper reporter and photographer passed the road and spotted Simon and his rustic wheelbarrow. He stopped, made pictures, and printed them in the newspaper with a short story about

Simon's living conditions. Several people responded, bringing him food, household items, and a little cash.

One of Simon's benefactors proved to be a wealthy widow from town, Mrs. Erpsides, who took a personal interest in Simon's welfare. In her chauffeured limousine, she brought boxes of goods and gave him a small amount of cash. She paid a nurse to come out and try to minister to his health needs, but the nurse gave up. On one visit Mrs. Erpsides slipped a big ring on his finger, telling him it would bring him good luck and that he could sell it for money if he ever needed to. To Simon it was just a "purty" play thing, but he agreed to keep it on his finger.

Other reports indicate the ring was big, beautiful, and very valuable. "It was almost pure gold and studded with fine diamonds," one man said. "Simon didn't care anything about it, nor did Mrs. Erpsides. She probably had a drawer full just as expensive as that one."

An accident happened at the sawmill one winter morning.

Simon was offbearing. He picked up a heavy slab. His foot slipped. He lost his balance. He fell forward, throwing out his arm and hand to break his fall. Instead his hand jammed into the whirling saw, which in a fraction of a second cut through his wrist. Simon screamed and lunged backward, his stumpy arm aloft, blood spattering everywhere.

They shut down the sawmill. The workers crowded around to help. One tied a tourniquet low on Simon's arm to stop the bleeding. "Load 'im in the truck and we'll drive 'im to the hospital in town," the sawyer ordered.

"No!" Simon objected. He refused to go to the doctor or hospital. He made them retrieve his severed hand, clean it, and tie it back in place under pressure. One man walked with him back to his shack and stayed a while. Simon gathered herbs from his premises, pounded them into a pulp, and applied this to his wound. He used baling twine, wire, and an old leather belt to tie around the hand's thumb and fingers and his elbow. This pressure kept the hand tightly in place. He wandered farther afield looking for herbs to heal and re-connect his hand to his arm.

But nothing worked. Infection set in. Slowly the hand rotted and putrefied. One day it fell off while he walked in the woods, and he didn't discover it missing until he got back to his shack. From then on, he spent most of his time looking for that rotted-off hand. Demented and senile now, he roamed the woods many a night, holding high his lighted kerosene lantern, trying desperately to find that lost hand which he wanted to reattach to his arm. Neighbors and passersby saw the light bobbing around in the darkness. They sympathized with ol' Sim. nobody wanted to help him.

He never found his rotted-off hand.

Now, his ghost keeps on looking.

Simon lived for maybe a couple of years after the accident. His last miserable year found him consumed with grief, pain, and infirmities. But crazy ol' Simon still roamed the woods, sometimes stopping in the wee hours at a neighbor's house, seeking help in his hunt for his lost hand. Early one winter, a hunter mistook him for a deer and shot and killed the old man.

A year or so later, the ghost light began appearing at night amid the hills and hollers—and it continues to this day. All the locals interpret it as the ghost of ol' Simon with his lantern out looking for his lost hand.

One bit of speculation might give impetus to the ghost's search. And it might generate interest among non-ghosts.

Did a finger on the severed hand still contain the ring that the wealthy widow, Mrs. Erpsides, slipped on it—the valuable gold ring studded with diamonds?

No one knows for sure. But the speculation is strong enough to bring some live assistance to Simon in his search. Even using modern gold and metal detectors, no one has yet found the hand and ring.

And they won't. I know. Because I am the one who will find it.

You see, I recently noticed something I hadn't seen before.

Every time I go out my back door, I can see this large, rusty old saw leaning against the smokehouse wall beside the door. Forty-one inches in diameter. A one-tooth-per-three-inches cutting edge. Forty-two teeth in all. A two-inch shaft hole in the center. One-eighth of an inch thick. Heavy. It must weigh twenty-five pounds. Through the years I've taken the saw for granted, pleased that it adds appeal to the smokehouse walls now covered with country graffiti, but hardly ever giving it a second glance.

All that changed abruptly when I noticed a peculiar spot on the face of the saw.

I bent low, then kneeled and examined it closely. Amid the scaly rust and bird droppings, one blotchy patch looked darker, thicker, reddish but different from the other rust. My fingers brushed over it lightly. Strange sensation. Something was trying to communicate. The longer I stared at that spot, the more the texture seemed to change. Then it hit me! Blood! It was a blood stain, human blood which splattered all over this saw when it amputated Simon's hand at the wrist. The bloodstains had remained on the saw, resisting the rust, then eventually fusing with it in some sort of reaction which created this special spot.

Now I look at the spot every day. It's changing. A pattern is emerging. I know what is happening, too.

Lines are forming. Objects are beginning to appear—a path, trees, brush, rocks, a stump, a stream. Kinda like a map. That's it! A map showing where the ring and the remains of the hand can be found. Not clear enough yet, but every day it improves a little. I already know the terrain pretty well. When the map clears up enough that I can recognize the spot, I'll go recover the ring and the remains of the hand.

But wait a minute! What will such a removal do to Simon's ghost?

He won't care about the ring, but if I can find and remove all the remains of that rotted-off hand that Simon's ghost has been looking for all these long years—it may remove the ghost, too. The ghost would have no more reason to keep searching, at least in that location.

So I won't do that. I'll keep the ring (of course I'll never display it as I do the saw) and leave the fragile remains of the hand, perhaps even conceal them a little deeper in the forest floor litter where they will remain forever. We've grown accustomed to the ghost of ol' Simon. We like having him around.

There are more blotches.

With the ghost of ol' Simon still active, who knows?

Maybe another map will begin forming on the face of that old saw.

THE SQUEALING GHOST

Back in the pre-motor vehicle days when horse and mule drawn wagons and buggies constituted most of the traffic on country roads, two men embarked on a memorable journey along what is now NC Highway 740 between Badin and New London, North Carolina. They left Badin after dark one late-summer day, detoured for a few minutes by way of Palmerville, then went back out to the main road and on to New London.

They traveled in a rickety one-horse wagon pulled by an equally ancient mule named Rhodie. Rhodie walked at a leisurely pace, occasionally focusing her ears and snorting at some unseen object in the black night. Familiar with the road, she knew the way without any guidance from the two men who occupied a wooden plank bench across the front part of the wagon bed. Between them sat a quart of moonshine whiskey, which they took turns upending and smacking their lips. A wire-handled oil lantern glowed at one corner of the wagon to give faint illumination and to warn other wagoneers of their presence.

Their feelings and disposition considerably enhanced toward the liberal side by the jar of moonshine, the two men laughed, hollered, slapped each other on the shoulder or knee and mouthed slurred endearments to the old mule as if it was the object of their deepest affection. Then they burst out in fragments of song and even tried to whistle a tune, except their whistling didn't amount to much. One tried to quote a familiar four-line love poem to ol' Rhodie, but he never could get the lines straight so they would rhyme, and he gave up.

"I'm a-gonna sang myself right intuw yore heart–all night, too–" Baskin crooned to his pal, Tobin.

Tobin didn't like to be sung to.

"An' I'll kick your ___ right under the seat and stomp all that cooing stuff outta you," he retorted. "Sing 'Dixie' if you want to, but that's all I wanta hear."

Abruptly ol' Rhodie stopped and snorted, her ears jerking forward. The two men swayed on the seat, but caught their balance. Then they heard it.

Squealing hungry-like, a pig trotted into the lantern light beside the road. It reared up on its hind legs looking at them. Then it wheeled around in a circle or two, squealing all the while, before it reared back up imploringly.

"Damn! A loose pig," Baskin hollered. "Let's catch 'im."

"Yeah, let's take him home with us," Tobin agreed.

They lumbered off the wagon. One caught the squealing pig with no trouble. "Nice porker," he said admiringly. "He'll be ready to butcher by Christmas."

In the wagon bed, they had two burlap bags full of sweet potatoes and a tin tub full of apples to take to their families. They poured out one of the bags of potatoes on the floor of the wagon bed, placed the pig inside the bag, and tied the top shut with twine. Then they poured out the apples and put the tin tub over the sacked pig, penning it securely underneath.

"I'll sit on the tub to be sure he don't git out while you drive ol' Rhodie," Tobin volunteered.

That's the way they made the rest of the trip, trying to sing and whistle a blurry version of "Dixie" while the squealing pig accompanied them, bumping the inside of the tub and struggling to get loose. Tobin could hear the pig and feel him lunging into the inside top of the tub on which he sat.

It took a couple of hours, but when they got home in New London they called all their family members out to see their prize. A pig of this quality was a real bonus, worth a trip to go after all by itself.

With the family gathered round, Tobin jerked up the tub with a flourish to reveal the surprise.

But there was no surprise. No pig. No sack. Nothing. Just empty space.

Both men knelt to look closely. They turned the tub over and over. They looked all over, under, and around the wagon. Nothing. They cocked their ears and listened. Nothing.

Suddenly sober, the men began stammering to their family about how they caught the squealing pig, sacked it, penned it securely under the tin tub, then Tobin sat on it all the way home without even once getting off. And how they sang and whistled to it.

"No. It couldn't've got away," they mumbled again and again.

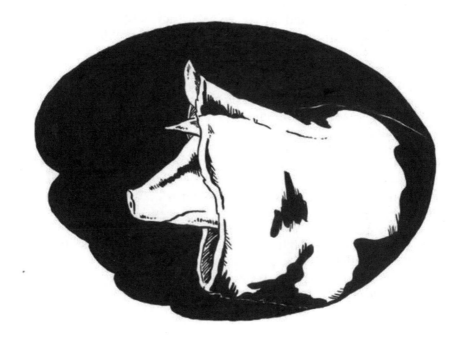

Yet there was absolutely no sign that a pig had ever been under that tub or in that wagon.

An older family member voiced a realization beginning to dawn on all of them:

"Maybe it was a ghost pig–"

Suddenly ol' Rhodie, tired from the night's trip, snorted and gave a long whinnying bray as if to emphasize the statement about the ghost.

The experience had a profound effect on both men. They stopped their moonshine drinking. They started going to church. They learned to sing with more dignity. They got jobs and provided for their families.

On subsequent trips to and from Badin, they asked everyone along the road about the mysterious pig. Nobody knew anything.

Later some people did report seeing a strange, squealing pig along the roadside at night. A few caught it, even placed it in their wagon or buggy, but it always disappeared by the time they got home.

Theories developed.

Maybe it really was a ghost pig. The ghost of a pig that somehow got separated from its mother and died of starvation while trying to find her along the roadside. This ghost pig is still looking for its mother and seeking help from passersby on the road.

"Food, that's what it wants," somebody says. "The next person who catches it can feed it and maybe it'll stay with them."

Somebody else says bring a live mother sow hog with a litter of new pigs along the road, and maybe this union will attract and pacify the ghost pig.

If you want to capture the ghost pig for a pet, or for any other reason, drive slowly along this highway at night. If you see the squealing ghost pig, stop and offer it an ear of corn.

Others say the best way to catch and keep the ghost pig is to learn how to sing and whistle "Dixie" better.

THE LAST GUGGLE

Most older folks are satisfied that they know why ghosts started prowling around the road near Junebug Holler in the Uwharries.

"It's the ghost of that ol' Connley Cruse, crazy and a-grieving so," the old folks say. "He'll pester folks on that road till Doomsday. Might as well leave it be and make a new road someplace else."

That's what happened, too, in later years. The old road was abandoned, as was Junebug Holler, the place where the junebugs gathered in the summertime. It got its name that way. All the junebugs in the territory—thousands of them—congregated there in season to feed on the honeysuckles and wild blooms. They were a nuisance. They lit and crawled on people, mules, and horses. Women shrieked and swatted and gamboled when a junebug dropped down the neck of their dresses and started crawling around. They say rowdy boys gathered junebugs by the lard-bucketful to take home and terrorize their sisters and other womenfolk. Even put some of the critters in the bedclothes.

Junebugs may have been partly responsible for turning ol' Connley Cruse into a ghost, too.

At least, that's what the old folks say.

Connley and his bride, Joybell, were married by the justice of the peace, ol' Petticord Burris, early on a bright Sunday morning in May. They hired Flambo Tucker to drive them in a surrey, pulled by a team of horses, to Rocky River Springs Resort to spend their honeymoon. Flambo was an experienced liveryman, but he had not recovered from a night of bottle-bibbing when he picked up the newlyweds and began the trip. The night of merrymaking left him unsteady and blurry-eyed.

As the surrey neared Junebug Holler about nine o'clock that morning, Flambo felt something clammy and clawy on his face and neck. He began some wild swatting and lost control of the trotting horses. The surrey wobbled off the road. The front wheel struck a stump, and the sudden lurch threw the occupants out.

Joybell's head struck a rock. She died within minutes.

Connley bounced over the buggy's broken wheel, flopped hard on the rocky ground, then tumbled over a time or two. He suffered a broken left arm, a bad gash on his leg, lacerations, and some internal injuries which plagued him the rest of his shortened life.

Gripped in a maniacal fury, Connley, despite his injuries, found the buggy whip and beat poor Flambo into a pulp, calling him a drunken and careless buzzard. Then Connley turned on the two horses and whiplashed their rumps raw before a passerby stopped and wrestled the whip away.

Flambo died, too, probably as much from the beating as from the buggy wreck injuries.

From that day on, Connley turned mean, exacting revenge on travelers on the Junebug Holler road. He patrolled the road intermittently, day and night, demanding that all travelers stop and let him inspect their conveyance. If he found whiskey or any type of strong drink, he took it and smashed the container against some rocks beside the road, not far from the boulder that caused Joybell's fatal injury. If he smelled alcohol on anyone's breath, he berated that individual with the vicious wrath of a crusading country preacher.

Lots of travelers objected to this usurpation of their rights. A few got fighting mad and threatened to shoot Connley. He ignored them. He kept right on smashing containers of strong drink and preaching to owners and imbibers. Travelers who came that way a second time usually sped up and tried to avoid Connley, which infuriated this disturbed man and intensified his viciousness toward the next wayfarer who possessed whiskey.

Gradually travelers stopped using the road, though it meant a substantial detour. Junebugs stopped coming to Junebug Holler. So did Connley. His internal injury from the buggy wreck affected his vital organs. His face turned a pale yellow. His hair came out. He coughed a lot and spat up blood. They found him dead one day, curled up beside the rock that caused his bride's death.

Except for sporadic local traffic, activity ceased around the Junebug Holler road. It was high time for some peace and quiet there, folks said, after all that trouble Connley Cruse had caused. Oldsters sat around the country store and around bright fireplaces and laughed at exaggerated versions of the deranged man's exploits. The tough old wagon road became eroded and overgrown.

The tranquillity didn't last long at Junebug Holler.

Boss Kennedy, who had traveled the road scores of times, stopped late one hot afternoon to get a drink of water from the spring. He left his two horses hitched to his wagon at the edge of the road.

Noise on the road attracted his attention.

"It sounded just like a wagon and mule, or a horse and buggy," he reflected later. "I could hear the wheels crunching over them rocks. I stepped out to see who it was. But it weren't nobody! Nothing a-tall! I could hear it good and plain. But I couldn't see nothing. An invisible noise. It went kinda rumbling on down the road out of hearing."

So confounded was Boss Kennedy that he hurried home to tell his family and all his neighbors about the mysterious noise at Junebug Holler.

Jethro Cunningham heard it next. And felt it.

"Just like Boss said, I heard it a-coming down the road. Sounded just like a hoss and buggy. It brushed by me just inches away. I felt the air and wind it caused. Just about pushed me backwards."

Lots of similar reports came after that. The curious came purposely to see if they could experience the ghost at Junebug Holler. Many of them claimed success.

One man said the invisible horse and buggy actually struck him and knocked him off the road. To prove it, he claimed to have sustained bruises and a lame leg.

Other adventuresome people claimed they were "run over" by the invisible but, apparently, quite solid horse and buggy.

Perceed Kendall was the first of many to report hearing other weird noises which corroborated what the older folks said. A religious man of middle age, he sometimes skipped church on Sunday mornings and drove his horse and buggy to this secluded spot to read his Bible and meditate. Something calamitous startled him out of his meditation about nine o'clock on a bright and mild morning.

"I've heard a buggy whip larruping against a hoss many a time, so I know that's what it was," he said emphatically. "Time after time that whip slapped down on that hoss's rump and that poor hoss whinnied and snorted like the Devil had 'im. After a while the whipping stopped. Then the buggy lurched forward with the hoss a-screaming in pain. That buggy crashed into something. Then I didn't hear no more. And I didn't see nothing, either."

Other visitors claimed they heard the buggy whip cutting into the body of Flambo Tucker, and heard Tucker screaming and moaning as the whip beat him almost to death.

"It's the ghost of ol' Connley Cruse still getting his revenge," the old folks said. "No telling how long his lust fer revenge will go on. I wouldn't wanna go there. You don't know when that whip might start beating on you!"

On and on, the ghost of Connley Cruse continued its real life counterpart's campaign against strong drink.

While not many strangers used the road anymore, some locals went there just to test the ghost's resolve and stamina.

They say you could pass along the old road on foot, on a bicycle, on horseback, in a mule or horse-drawn conveyance, early motorcar, or any other way, and if you had any whiskey or strong drink it didn't survive the passage. It wound up poured out and the container smashed on the rocks—the rocks near where the buggy wreck occurred.

"I seen it! I felt it," one man exclaimed. "Our whole family was riding by in the wagon. Broad daylight, too. I sat on the seat beside Pa. Pa didn't know it, but I had a pint of moonshine in my inside coat pocket. It just rose outta my pocket, floated through the air and busted to pieces on them rocks. Pa and the others heard and saw it smash, but they didn't know where it came from, thank goodness!"

No matter if it was small as a thimbleful or big as a hogshead, the vengeful ghost let no alcohol through.

This portion of the old road became littered with shattered glass and broken wooden keg staves.

One observer claimed the ghost made sure all the whiskey drained out of the containers right down to the last guggle.

"I saw it twice," he maintained. "A glass jug and a wooden keg. The bottom of the jug was broke over the rock, but the top half, pointed down, still had the cork in place and held whiskey. This part rose up. That cork came out. The whiskey guggled out to the last drop. The keg did the same thing. The bung came out and the rest of the whiskey guggled out."

How did the ghost deal with alcohol *inside* a traveler?

Vague reports suggest that some inebriated passersby were gripped and shaken so hard that they sobered up quickly.

Slosh Hartson knew all about this ghostiness at Junebug Holler. But it didn't bother him. He didn't believe in ghosts. All those reports were just tall tales and "'maginations" to him. He knew he could go through the holler anytime he wished without molestation. This trip would prove it.

An agile oldster with a drawly voice, he talked to his mule, Ol' Jule, as he buckled a beat-up saddle around her middle and tied two burlap bags to the horn. A round trip to the Flatwoods community required several hours. And to Flatwoods he had to go. Flatwoods' moonshiners produced the best whiskey in the county. They used the copper pot stills which turned out better quality moonshine than the submarine variety.

He had been dry for a month, and couldn't stand it any longer. It was time to catch up. A neighbor, Bentley Giles, financed the trip. "You know them folks," Bentley said. "Get us some of their best booze. I'll pay for it and give you half. You go get it and bring it back tonight."

He got there by mid-afternoon. The Lambert boys had two kegs of aged moonshine ready. He paid them and put each keg inside a burlap bag, tied it to the saddle horn and let it drape down along the mule's shoulder in front of his leg. Slosh persuaded the Lamberts to give him a pint to drink on the long ride back home.

By the time he approached Junebug Holler, the pint was empty and he could hardly stay in the saddle. His slurry voice serenaded the moon and Ol' Jule. Now the mule knew the way home without Slosh's fumbly attempts to guide him.

Abruptly, Ol' Jule whinnied and lurched to one side, almost throwing his rider from the saddle. Slosh clutched the horn as the mule sank to its knees, then teetered to the right and left. He heard the two kegs splinter under this pressure. He heard the distinct gurgle of the moonshine spilling out on the rocky ground. Frantically he tried to reach it, but one leg was penned under a stirrup, trapping him partly under the downed mule.

"No, no!" he moaned and groaned. He shouted and swore. "I gotta save it. Bentley will kill me if that booze is gone. Help me. Lawd, help me save it!"

But nothing helped Slosh Hartson save his moonshine.

Hours passed. Dawn began to lighten the eastern sky. Ol' Jule had risen out of the tangle and wandered off, leaving Slosh weakly stirring amid the splintered kegs and torn burlap bags.

Slosh hefted the remains of the bottom of one keg. Inside he saw the glint of liquid. Hardly a swallow. But he had to have it. He saw a tiny hole nearby. He tilted the keg remnant so the swallow of moonshine trickled into his mouth. He savored it right down to the last drop before something slapped the broken keg from his hands and away from his face. It slammed into the nearby rocks.

Today, the old Junebug Holler road still exists, but you'll never find it or recognize it. Don't even try. It's on private property and the owner has fenced it off and discourages any inquiry or visitation. Less than a handful of people are aware of its location. None of them talk.

Once in a great while the owner or a stout-hearted colleague will cross the fence and walk along what used to be the old wagon road with an open can or bottle of beer in his hand, just to see if the ghost will activate. Half the time it does. The beer can is slapped from his hands and clatters onto an overgrown heap where the remaining liquid guggles out. This individual hurries back out of the fenced area before the invisible hoss and buggy runs him down.

There is speculation that the vengeful ghost of Connley Cruse has relocated because of the lack of traffic at its original location.

Now you are apt to encounter this ghost, day or night, on any road, public or private, anywhere in the Uwharries.

The evidence is plain to see—empty beer and whiskey containers littering the roadsides. The ghost doesn't care where they land. He just wants the contents destroyed.

There's one sure way of telling if the ghost is about to target you or your vehicle. If you feel the sensation of the clammy, clawy junebug on your neck, which then drops under your collar—look out!

Those jolting vibrations you feel are not caused by bumps in the road, either. It's the ghost trying to shake some sense into those with alcohol on their breath.

So be forewarned. Even though the windows and doors of your vehicle are closed and locked, the ghost will levitate any container of alcohol out of the vehicle and dash it to the roadside where all the contents will pour out—right down to the last guggle.

SHADOWY GHOSTS

Shadows probably produce more ghosts than any other element in the Uwharries and elsewhere. This includes both solar and lunar shadows. However, nighttime enhances the uneasiness and eeriness when you wonder what the darkness harbors. Apprehension increases when you're traveling a lonely road at midnight and face a series of deep mooncast shadows across the way ahead. You feel vulnerable, as if entering a new dimension of incomprehensible mystery.

Sometimes the shivers start.

Five of us rowdy boys experienced a shadowy ghost a long time ago, and we have been believers ever since. Every dark spot across the road re-enforces our conviction that ghosts and shadowy lairs coincide.

That fall night in the late 1930s, we huddled in the shoulder-high scrub pines on the high bank at the north end of Buzzard Hill. Below us Coble's Mill Road, with its two wheel paths shining like twin ribbons in the moonlight, wound down the hill to the Rocky River. Heavy bridge timbers rattled as vehicles crossed the steel-structured bridge linking Stanly and Union counties. Close to midnight on this Saturday, only an occasional car passed, with maybe a wagon or buggy in between.

Cars coming our way across the bridge picked up speed to gain momentum for the long uphill stretch. We liked this steady speed and predictable slowing as the cars struggled against the hill's steep resistance. Vehicles coming down the hill often braked erratically which threw off our timing.

For a year or so the Jones boys, Elmer and Cutie Coley, and I had bombarded vehicles passing this location. This high bank with brush and scrub pines choking the view made a perfect launching place for throwing objects to spatter on the passing cars and other vehicles—whenever our timing was right. Things like heavy cornshucks, tomatoes, squash, hunks of melon and pumpkins, wormy apples, peaches, pears, walnuts, mud balls, green cotton boles, and corncobs. We enjoyed the challenge of heaving these objects high in the air over the road and timing their landing exactly with the arrival of the vehicle directly even with us below.

This required skill. And practice. The more sophisticated projectiles in our arsenal were entrusted only to the the best of our hurlers. In fact, the best of our group made a decorated bombardier in World War II, enviably known for his target-splitting skill with the bomb load—some of which could be traced to latent ability developed on the slopes of Buzzard Hill.

The results of this bombing on Coble Mill Road were a sight to see. Of course this is just what kept us juvenile knaves at it. Not often did we cause much actual damage to the vehicles. We just soiled and spattered them, and scared the occupants.

Usually when we scored a hit, or near hit, the vehicle stopped and the driver and occupants boiled out to see what had happened and inspect the damage. Quickly they looked all around, but they could see no sign of life in the gloom, though they often eyed the high bank with suspicion. Often the men swore and shook their fists toward the bank. Now and then a man got mad enough to scramble up the bank to chase down the vandals he suspected it of harboring. None ever succeeded. Day or night, no one person could ever catch us in these dense river hills we knew so well.

Probably the most fun we had was with the wagons, buggies, and Hoover carts drawn by horses and mules. Those animals are skittish at night and easily frightened into stampeding. For them we kept ready several tightly wound balls of string and cloth strips, with thin dangles hanging loose. When one of these came fluttering and whooshing down near the head of a horse, it panicked. We saw hellacious runaways.

Naturally all this nocturnal activity intensified rumors and fears in the community about the location being han'ted and being the lair of the supernatural.

Some people linked the goings-on with the acrimony and venom of an old witch woman who sometimes chased us boys with a butcher knife from her decaying home up from the river. Superstitious people claimed the old witch woman had cast a spell on the river bridge area, and this explained all the mysterious bombardment.

We were elated at all the notoriety we stirred up.

Strangely, no one ever caught us. Our parents never found out about our shenanigans.

Most, if not all of us, would have wound up in reformatories or the penitentiary if we had kept going the way we were headed. Fortunately our destinies changed abruptly on this moonlit night at the Coble Mill end of Buzzard Hill.

Primed and ready for our next victim, we quietly awaited the sound of a motor or the rumbling of wheels in the distance, but none came. Then we heard voices. Out on the bridge. Two people walked toward us, talking as they came. We could hear animated voices, and laughter now and then.

The pedestrians came closer, off the bridge and up the grade, walking abreast in the wheel paths. Moonlight outlined them sharp and clear against the packed roadbed. We could not identify them or understand their conversation. Tacitly we decided not to attack and let them pass unmolested.

Almost directly below us lay a deep shadow cast over the road by a big pine tree. We often used it as a reference point in hurling our projectiles. Now we simply hunched down in the pines and watched as the two talking figures came to this slash of darkness across the road.

All of us saw and heard them enter the shadow, and expected them to emerge a few seconds later on the other side.

But they didn't come out of the shadow!

It swallowed them completely. We waited and waited. Several minutes passed with no sign of the two people who walked into the shadow.

We didn't take our eyes off that shadow. The ends of it extended only a short ways beyond either edge of the road. No one backtracked out of it. No one emerged. No one went sideways out of it.

All of us scrambled down the bank for a closer look.

Reaching road level, we fanned out, crisscrossing the shadow and combing down all the side ditches, bushes, and banks. There was no sign of anyone. But no one could have escaped from this shadow without us seeing them. It wasn't possible.

Yet where were the two figures we had plainly seen and heard walk into it?

The trees whispered dark secrets around us. Brittle moonlight painted us with palish gold. River water in the mill pond swished more ominously over the dam. Frogs croaked a mournful dirge in the still water.

Two of my buddies trembled. Another muttered incoherently. I felt my own heart pounding wildly.

Suddenly it dawned on us that maybe we had overstayed our welcome here.

Would the shadow swallow *us* if we hung around?

"This place is really han'ted," Cutie Coley squalled. "Let's git fer home!"

Like a stampeding bunch of antelopes, we skeedaddled.

Later we talked it over many times. The only conclusion we reached was that the mysterious vanishing act had been a warning for us to stop our mischief and mend our way of living. Which we all did.

My four buddies are all dead and gone now. But many times while they were alive I heard them vow that they witnessed two talkative pedestrians disappear into that tree shadow across the roadway and never come out.

From that day onward, the bombardment and mischief by a rowdy quintet stopped, and as far as I know, all has been peaceful on the roadway by Buzzard Hill ever since.

But I can't help wondering.

Could other mysterious disappearances be attributed to a shadow?

Are there other swallowing shadows lurking in the Uwharries?

I don't know about you, but when I'm out traveling alone, I hurry through the deepest shadows across the road.

Especially at night.

THE PARTYING GHOSTS

Want to go partying with a ghost?

Make that plural. Partying with ghosts? A group of ghosts?

You have that option if you wish to go prowling around through the Narrows Gorge on the Yadkin River near Badin, North Carolina. This lonely but strikingly beautiful wilderness area lies in the heart of central North Carolina's Uwharrie Mountains.

You'll have to go prowling at night, too, for this ghost party materializes only then, as far as anyone knows.

While others have experienced it and been scared out of their wits, two Montgomery County fishermen reported their encounter with the ghost party in the most graphic detail. Till their dying day, they told about it with utmost sincerity and, while they never did return, with the conviction that anyone could experience this ghost party if they had the gumption and repeated at least some of the actions which they believed caused the ghosts to appear.

Tired after a day's work, they arrived at Falls Lake behind Narrows Dam on a late summer afternoon. They left their pickup truck parked beside the twisty mountain road, and took a trail down through the rocks to the river's edge. They set up their two-man tent, unrolled their sleeping bags, and got fishing gear into action. There was just enough chill in the air to make a campfire feel good. Soon they had caught enough bass for their supper, and the aroma of sizzling fish wafted through the misty night air.

For the next several hours after eating, they alternated between fishing and relaxing and napping before the fire and in their sleeping bags. Hooting owls punctuated the swish of the river water, lulling their senses. An almost full moon rose over the trees across the river. They could hear the faint hum of the generators in the Narrows Dam powerhouse a ways upstream.

Once or twice they thought they spotted a light up on the mountainside near the old road they had descended. Maybe it was the headlights of another fisherman's vehicle, but nobody else ever showed up.

Along about midnight, the two men grew weary and were about ready to break camp and go home. The fish had stopped biting, although they already had caught a nice string of fish, enough to take home and show off to neighbors. A feeling of restlessness and frustration hung in the air and interfered with their sleeping.

"Let's walk back to the truck and get us a beer," one said. "If that don't help us go to sleep, then we'll just load up and leave."

They scrambled up the bank through the rocks to the old road, but they paused when they saw an eerie light illuminating a small clearing amid the brush and trees beyond the parked truck. "There's some people up there. Let's go closer and see what they're doing," one said.

They moved closer, on past their truck, then stopped and looked. What they saw imprinted on their minds for the remainder of their lives. Many times they told this story to friends.

"There were people, a whole bunch of people—at least a dozen or more. Yes, they were kinda smoky, kinda misty like. But definite, ordinary people. They moved around a campfire. Lighted lanterns hung from tree limbs. We heard low voices—couldn't understand the words too well—just low voices—and it sounded like one woman's voice, too. Some were dancing. One man buck dancing and clapping his hands. Some music, too, like a record player. A slow, soft soloist, with a woman joining in some. All of them seemed to be smiling and laughing. Kinda swinging and waltzing in slow motion, too.

"Food, plenty of it. We could see and smell the food. And smell the whiskey. They were cooking meat, fish, chicken. A big pot of stew. Big coffee urn. A keg of whiskey hung from a limb. Most people either had in their hands a plate of food or a mug, cup, or glass. Looked like there was a big wooden barrel full of crushed ice. Big trays full of peanuts, fruit, and pastries. One man pulled out a small accordion and started playing some polkas. It looked like a birthday party, a wedding party, or just a big party to celebrate something, but surely an all-night party."

After watching for a few minutes, the two men decided they'd like to join the party. Heck, partying all night was better than fishing all night, anyhow. "Let's go back to the truck and get our beer," one said. "If we bring some beer, maybe they'll let us join the fun."

They walked back to the truck and lifted out the beer. They turned to walk back to the party, but stopped.

There was no party. It had vanished. Completely.

Gone was all the light, sound, movement, and smells. All they saw were dark trees and brush, faintly illuminated by silvery streaks of moonlight. An owl hooted. Frogs croaked down at the river. A lonely, far-off, mournful howl sounded like it might have come from a coyote. The breeze had more chill in it, causing the men to shiver and shake. The leaves and branches rustled in a sinister way. Now the swishing of the river communicated a warning.

Too scared to scream, the two men could only jabber, mumble in utter confusion, fling their arms and point.

They dropped their beer and trampled upon it as they scrambled back toward the truck.

One slipped, fell, and skinned his knee.

They muttered, "But we saw them–all them people–moving all around–the food–the booze–the music–singing–laughing–"

One man beat his palms on the hood of the truck.

"Sure they were real–real as anything I ever saw in my life. But where did they go to? How could they leave that fast? Maybe they saw us. Yeah, they found out they were being watched and they disappeared."

Then it dawned on them.

Ghosts!

"Gawd-a-mighty!" one hollered. "Ghosts! I've heard this place was han'ted. Let's get outta this crazy place! Ghosts–"

The other man wanted to retrieve their camping and fishing gear.

"Hell with the gear–I'm gittin' outta here. Jump in that truck if you're going with me."

Their trip home was the fastest on record.

The two Montgomery Countians never came back to Narrows Gorge, although the tales they told of their experience surely brought others.

People pondered about it for a long time.

Before he died many years back, Clancy Purcell came closest to explaining the ghosts of the Narrows Gorge. And Clancy made it clear right quick that what he told was not gospel truth, but just what he had heard and picked up during his years of working in and around the gorge with hundreds of other laborers.

"It started way back when they were building the dam and powerhouse and the whole plant. They had hundreds and hundreds of workers here from several countries. They worked us hard and long and the bosses and foremen were tough and mean. The pay was decent enough, but man, they expected you to work hard and long every day and every day. Ol' Kidd Heavy was their policeman. If you didn't show up, he'd come and roust you, no matter what, and run you in right to the job. He wore a gun, rode a horse, even threatened to zap you on the backside with his whip. Mean ol' sucker. Nobody crossed him.

"Well, this one work gang–twenty-five or thirty men–really had it the worst. They had the toughest, meanest job of all. Somebody got killed every now and then, some in places where the body couldn't be recovered. No work ever stopped. They just kept on a-working. The bosses, the foremen too, drove 'em like a herd of cows or horses. Cussed 'em, called 'em vile names, worked 'em hard ten hours a day, seven days a week, for months at a time. Hardly ever got a day off. These men complained and groused and protested, but never enough to do any good.

"Finally after a couple of months of ten-hour days with no time off, they'd had enough. A leader rose up in their ranks. Fine young man. A furriner. Name of Bernstien, Burnie Bernstien, from Italy or Spain or France–one of them countries. He had a classy name. Born leader. Everybody liked him. They listened to him. He says we're gonna rebel, gonna strike, gonna take ourselves–every last one of us–a party for a night or two, no matter what they do or say. And the bosses and the foreman, they are not invited.

"Burnie tried to negotiate with the foreman. No luck. He went to see the boss, a man named Pompano or something like that. Pompano flew into a fury, cussed and kicked Burnie out of the office, telling him he would be docked for every minute away from the job. Then Burnie called all the men together at the end of the shift and they planned their secret party. Everybody sworn to secrecy. Everybody given a job–something to bring or do or see about. Everybody enthusiastic. They would party all night, then all day, and if that weren't enough, they'd do it another night and day before going back to work. And from then on, they'd do it at least once a month. And Burnie made it clear. He was the leader. He'd take the rap no matter how management responded.

"Party night came and all the work gang members participated. They picked a real isolated spot back off the gorge road in a little holler surrounded by plenty of trees and ridges to hide all the light and noise. When the gang didn't show up for work, the foreman grew livid with rage. He notified Kidd Heavy, Pompano, and other management and security people. They conducted an extensive search for the missing workers. None were found. Pompano grew stomping mad and went off searching by himself, mumbling that he'd find them, probably kill half of them, and put the other half back to work, making them work doubly hard.

"Along about midnight the party was going good and everybody was enjoying this blessed respite from the work site. Suddenly from out of the blackness, a ranting and raving figure burst into the circle of light. It was Pompano, waving a big pistol in one hand and a flashlight in the other. Swaggering around and brandishing his pistol, he began cussing and demonizing the men, using the most vile language anyone ever heard. A few men started to speak up, but he shouted them down. All that would satisfy him was for every last man to leave this minute and run back to the job site, and work doubly hard to make up for the lost time.

"Burnie stood up and tried to speak politely. But Pompano wheeled toward him, leveled his pistol and fired. Burnie slumped to the ground, a bullet lodged in his chest near his heart. Two dozen men quickly advanced on Pompano, who dropped his gun and began backing up. Armed with tools, clubs, guns, and lanterns, the men hemmed Pompano in a tight semi-circle and forced him to the brink of a seventy-five-foot cliff which dropped off to the rocks at the river's edge. He realized what was happening and tried to plead with the men, telling them they would all be charged with murder. Rather than face the raised clubs, he backed up until he lost his footing, then fell, screaming, over the cliff. They heard his body splat on the rocks below. Short swishes of the river water applauded the action.

"That was the official version of what happened—Pompano lost his footing and fell to his death. How do you charge two dozen men with murder?

"Burnie was dying when they got back to him. But he lived long enough to talk a little. He talked about coming back. As a ghost. As a ghost leader. He could keep on helping his friends this way. He said every man who had died on this construction so far and every man who died on it from now to the end would come back as a ghost. He would recruit them, train them, and lead them. Their main function would be to torment and harass foremen and bosses who were mean and cruel to the workers. And they, the ghosts, could resume their partying anytime they wanted to.

"I'm here to tell you, working conditions improved after that."

Clancy didn't know, maybe nobody does, the total number of deaths that occurred during the construction of the dam and powerhouse, the nearby plant, the two villages, schools, business buildings, and other facilities. Some estimates are as high as a dozen; others at two score and more. Accidental, violent deaths since then have added to the ghostly gallery. Burnie is still on the job, welcoming each new arrival and coordinating their activities. While they ghost at other places, usually associated with their death or fatal injury location, their favorite ghosting place is still the Narrows Gorge.

That's where you are more likely to encounter them, as did the two men from Montgomery County.

Since those early days of construction and plant operation, working conditions have improved a lot. No longer do bosses cuss the workers and abuse them physically and emotionally. So, while Burnie and his ghosts still monitor everything pretty closely, most of their ghosting takes place in the woods along the twisty access road by the rim of the gorge, the road leading to the fishing area back of the dam and powerhouse. Here they enjoy their ghostly parties without interference. Since their original party was interrupted, they regroup here to do it over again and again.

However, these ghosts claim the entire gorge and surrounding area as their own private ghosting territory, extending on to the villages and big plant. Away from the gorge, if one ghost needs help, Burnie is quick to send assistance. In life, close teamwork was mandated for survival. Now they keep it going in the afterlife. Never pick a fight with a ghost or try to heckle him, especially one of Burnie's ghosts at the Narrows. He's taught them tactics unknown to mere mortals.

These ghosts of the Narrows Gorge have a built-in distrust and dislike for authority. So if you are an authority figure, it's best to keep a low profile while in their territory.

And if you're a mean person, guilty of murder or any other heinous crime, even in your heart, don't stray to the cliff edge on top of the gorge. You may find yourself hemmed in by unseen forces pushing you over the brink.

There's the international flavor, too.

Apparently the ghosts rotate their parties and theme them—the food, dress, music, singing, dancing, drinking—according to the culture represented in their membership. Burnie is always looking for greater quality and superior showmanship. If you're a good performer, and if your ancestry coincides with their theme, and if you wander into their party at the right time, Burnie might like you so much that he'll keep you and make you one of them and never let you come back. As a human.

THE GOLD NUGGET

I got carried away by this rawboned old-timer lounging on the front porch of his tumbledown shack, deep in the Uwharries. What triggered this fascination and sustained it was a nugget of gold bigger than a golf ball, which he fondled in gnarled hands. He held the gleaming gold up in front of him and contemplated it as one would a cherished picture or memento.

He even let me hold it in my hands for a moment.

I had stopped to ask directions, expecting to be there only a few minutes, but that nugget of pure Uwharrie gold so mesmerized me that I stayed for an hour....

*　　*　　*

It took me a long time, but I finally pieced together highlights of one version of the Moat Pierce family slaughter. Horrendous. One of the goriest I have encountered. I shudder as much from the gore as from the ghost.

A prospector of renown, Moat scoured the Uwharrie hills for gold—and he found a lot. He traded some of it at the general store and sold some of it at the gold mine in the area. Impressed by his finds, the miners and assayers tried to get Moat to pinpoint the location of his finer specimens. But he would never divulge these sites. He accumulated enough gold to provide for his family and keep himself happy, and that's all he cared about. He wanted no part of any big scale mining operations. Nor any small partners. He was satisfied just doing everything himself.

But a few individuals who knew about Moat's success weren't satisfied to let it go at that. Unable to find much gold themselves, they wanted more of what Moat had. And they wanted it the easy way.

They began pestering Moat about revealing locations where they could find more gold. He refused. They accosted Moat on a lonely trail and roughed him up to make him tell. He refused. Later they threatened to kill him if he didn't tell them what they wanted to hear. They even threatened to kill his family. Moat told them he would never give them what they wanted. He swore eternal vengeance upon his tormentors if they ever harmed him or his family.

They tried to follow him and learn his secret gold panning places. An expert woodsman, Moat knew when he was being followed and observed. He went to unproductive places to fool his followers.

Showdown time came.

The plotters, a greedy trio, went to Moat's cabin while he was away to intimidate his family. Maybe they could be scared into talking about those secret places. But they refused. Moat had warned them. Not even a shotgun waved and pointed in their faces would make them talk.

Infuriated by this refusal, the three instigators ransacked the house, and bludgeoned and stabbed the family to death—a mother and two children—leaving blood splattered all over the walls and floor.

They say Moat went half-crazy when he came home at dusk and found his family slaughtered like animals.

After the funeral, he grabbed his rifle and hid in the bushes and foliage along the trails frequented by the murderers. From ambush he picked them off, one by one. He hid the bodies where they were never found. After salvaging what he wanted, Moat burned his cabin to the ground and started living in the woods where no one could find him. Rarely was he seen anywhere, except when he bought supplies at the general store and sold his gold nuggets at the gold mines.

But some relatives of the slain murderers wanted Moat dead or alive. They wanted him alive first because, being prospectors themselves, they intended to force him to reveal the sources of his gold. They surprised and overpowered him at his campfire one night. For an hour they grilled and threatened him. He wouldn't talk, except to curse them and swear revenge. They burned his feet in the fire. They used a funnel and poured huge quantities of water down his throat. They broke one arm, then the other. As he neared unconsciousness, still without revealing his secret, they shot and killed him, leaving his body to rot beside the campfire.

A year or so later is when the ghosting started.

Folks say the ghost of Moat Pierce was vicious at first until it accomplished its primary purpose. Then it turned benevolent and remains so today, and will continue to until its mission is completed.

All three of Moat's murderers met with bad luck. It started gradually, then intensified until it took their lives. One took a fatal tumble off a cliff. One drowned in the Uwharrie River. The last one died when a tree fell on top of him.

"Oh, just accidents, I reckon," some folks said.

After that the ghost didn't bother anybody, but it did help a few.

Now and then a deserving prospector would be guided into a more lucrative location to look for gold. Nothing big. No sensational finds. Just enough to make it worthwhile.

Goldpanners wondered if the ghost would ever guide anyone to that special place that had yielded so much impressive gold for Moat Pierce. Would the ghost become that benevolent? To whom would he reveal it?

For a while more goldpanners than ever sifted the graveled streams, each hoping he would be the favored one. Eventually interest slackened and only the dedicated prospectors continued.

Apparently the ghost did help once, deep inside a gold mine.

The main gold vein the miners were working dead-ended, and no one could find where it resumed. The rest of the veins were just borderline profitable. There was talk of closing down the mine. One laborer who had been working on the side of the horizontal tunnel paused to rest for a moment. He said he felt something force him to turn around and take a step or two, then face the opposite wall. The invisible force literally raised the pick in his hands and made him take a few licks into the wall. Revealed there in the glimmering light were chunks of gold from a vein richer than any yet discovered, a vein rich enough to keep the mine operating for at least another year.

There was talk of another ghost, a related ghost, in this part of the Uwharries.

On mild nights on some of the rough roads and trails used by the prospectors, you could see a woman and two children walking and stopping to peer into the bushes, as if they expected to find someone. "It's the ghosts of his family—his wife and children," a mother moaned. "Why, oh, why can't they be reunited?"

Maybe they were reunited in the spirit world. After a while the family ghosts were not seen much anymore.

But the ghost of Moat Pierce still prowls around. Folks say you're apt to see him most anywhere there's gold or talk of gold. He's waiting for just the right person to reveal his big secret to. Everyone agrees that he *will* reveal his secret—the place where he found his big nugget and the place where there's oodles more—before he stops ghosting.

Yet for the time being, he seems to enjoy tantalizing people. Certain people, that is.

*   *   *

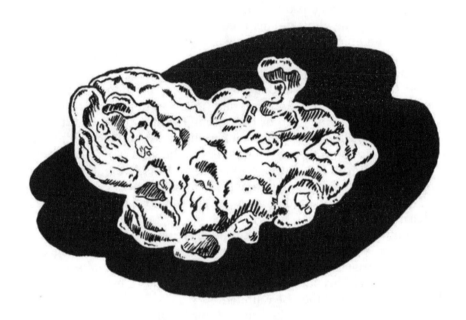

The day I spotted the old man lounging on his front porch, I was lost in a part of the Uwharries where I had never been. The twisty old road grew narrower and rougher. I expected it to dead end, meaning a long backtrack for me. So when I spotted this man, the first sign of life or residence in at least a mile, I immediately stopped to ask for directions. I had to park my truck, then walk a ways to reach his shack, which appeared to be partly hidden in some bushes.

I waved a friendly gesture, then greeted him. He responded and invited me to sit a spell. He wore a tank-top shirt, which revealed long arms and neck. A grizzled beard covered most of his face. The majority of his sweaty gray hair hid under a greasy felt hat. His eyes glinted sharply. Big hands gesticulated. He sat on what looked like the remains of a living room couch, his scarred boots propped on a rail between two support posts.

When I sat on the ragged edge of the porch floor, it swayed and creaked under my weight. The old man chuckled. His weight didn't seem to bother anything.

Having obtained the information I needed, I was ready to leave when I spotted a rusty gold panning pan hanging on a nail in the wall.

"Much prospecting for gold around here?" I asked, nodding toward the pan.

"Yeah, people look for gold hereabouts," he said. His voice sounded crisp as a hard apple being sliced.

"Is it mostly gold panning like this?" I said, again indicating the pan.

"Yeah, mostly gold panning in the creeks. The mines, they done played out."

"Anything impressive found around here? Any big stuff?" I asked.

He looked at me hard for a moment, as if evaluating something.

Slowly he rose, stretched a bit, then reached up into the murkiness of the unsealed porch framework overhead. His rough hands came down with something cupped in them.

"Hold out your hand," he ordered. "Both of them."

I cupped my hands in front of him.

He dropped an object, which made my hands dip until I counteracted the weight. I held a nugget of almost pure gold, at least twice as big as a golf ball. Amazed, I raised it to eye level.

The surface was not smooth as a golf ball. It was slightly pitted and ridged, dimpled and pimpled. It gleamed and shimmered as I turned it over and over. I estimated it to be ninety-five percent pure. And heavy. It was as heavy as dozens of golf balls. I had seen raw gold before, but never a specimen so illustrious.

The old man was pleased at my reaction of surprise and shock, at my open mouth and bulging eyes, at my expression of disbelief.

Recovered a bit, I asked another question. "Where did you find this beautiful ball of gold?"

Some of the pleasantness left his face. He regarded me intently for a moment.

"Out there," he said, waving his big hand.

Out there was a dozen square miles of Uwharrie wilderness.

Reluctantly I returned the heavy nugget to his hands and prepared to leave. He replaced it amid the rafters over the porch floor, before turning and waving goodbye.

As I neared my truck, instinct told me to turn and take a last look.

Everything had vanished. No old man. No porch. No shack. No sign of any habitation. Nothing there but typical Uwharrie trees and undergrowth. I could not believe my eyes or my wildly thumping heart. I stumbled around for a moment or two, dazed and uncomprehending, before I drove away.

The only conclusion I can reach is that I am not the right person that the ghost of Moat Pierce is looking for.

Maybe you will be.

MEANER THAN THE DEVIL

Whenever it thunders I am reminded of the ghosts around the old Mordecia Slasher homeplace in the Uwharries. I've never been there. I couldn't find it. Research didn't help. Folklore and hand-me-downs are all I have to go on, but its reality is beyond question in my mind. It's part of my consciousness. My consciousness plays no tricks. When it encapsulates an idea or image, that's final.

So when the whole world, the whole universe, outside my window vibrates with booming, crack-a-ling, rolling thunder, I can hear pitiful, ghostly voices pleading with a monster to stop his torture and give them some peace. But he never stops. The pleading never stops.

Perhaps you can hear them, too, if you listen closely.

All Mordecia Slasher wanted his entire adult life was to become a warlock. He was convinced that the more wicked he acted, the greater were his chances of succeeding. Practicing this philosophy made life hellish for his family and those around him. Even the animals. Some say his depravity multiplied every day.

"You've heard of mean men?" an old-timer said. "Well, he wasn't just mean; he was the very devil himself. There couldn't be any devil any meaner than that man. Somebody oughta a-bushwhacked 'im when he was a yearling."

The weather-blackened Slasher farm house sat amid a bunch of outbuildings, pastures, fields, and a straggle of orchard, all struggling against the elements and in desperate need of repair. Day or night, passersby could see and hear disturbing sights and sounds coming from the premises. There were no screens on the doors and windows, which stood open, allowing free access to bugs and pests, even stray animals. Cats frequented every room. Slasher permitted only meager light at night, an oil lamp or lantern turned low, a candle, or light from the fireplace on which most of the cooking was done.

"The family froze in cold weather," the old-timer continued. "Stingy, man, he was stingy. Wouldn't let 'em burn but just one little stick of wood at a time in the fireplace. He starved 'em almost to death. His animals and livestock, too. No hired help would stay more than a day or two. He watched over every bite they took, every swallow of water. Somebody said they got by on a biscuit a day and a cup of water.

"But beatings–them beatings–

"He beat his wife and children just about every day. With a leather strap. With a big switch, a pole, rope, a bed slat, a chair. Anything he could pick up. Them poor children. That poor woman. I've seen 'em hobbling out in the yard, crawling, bleeding, throwing up, crying their hearts out and begging 'im to stop. He'd just laugh and gloat and whup 'em harder. He even whupped 'em at night in bed, and they had to stay there all night, a bloody body in a bloody bed.

"Why they didn't kill the bastard, I'll never know. They shoulda slit his throat, shot 'im, brained 'im with a sledge hammer, stuffed 'im down that old well, cut his carcass up into little pieces and fed it to the dogs. But they couldn't. They weren't strong enough. That's why they didn't run away. Too weak. He kept 'em beaten up, half crippled, half sick, starved. No money, hardly any clothes and shoes. Anyway, not much did they ever get out of his sight."

People passing by claimed they could hear crying, sobbing, wailing coming from the premises. Also frantic squalling and pleading: "Don't hit me no more!" "Pa, please stop it!"

From the barn you could hear the horse and mule, penned in their stalls, squealing in agony as Slasher beat them with a board and gouged them with a pitchfork. Always the cows and hogs were mooing and squealing in hunger.

Then Slasher began a new tactic.

He sent for witches and invited them into his home. Many a night he spent cavorting with the witches while his family huddled fearfully in another room. He insisted that the witches teach him and coax him in all requirements necessary to become a warlock. He must have pleased them sufficiently because they cooperated. For him their instructions were: the meaner, the better.

He grew meaner and meaner.

One or two of his oldest daughters had babies, presumably sired by their father. An older son was forced to have sexual relations with his mother.

Later the wife and mother, sick and emaciated, collapsed and died in the yard. They drug her inside. The older daughters wouldn't let neighbor women help prepare the body for burial. They did not want anyone else to see the livid scars, old and new, covering their mother's body. Unceremoniously they buried her in the edge of the yard.

Slasher continued, even increased, his horrific torture to the remaining family, his children. The meaner, the better. He was determined to earn warlock status.

Here's where the enigma arises. Most people don't believe it. Yet a few do. It was told and talked about. It was rumored and handed down. Did it really happen? Maybe. Maybe not.

The devil himself came to the Slasher household. More than once. Apparently to help Slasher attain warlockhood.

"Yeah, he did, that's right," the old-timer continued. "The witches helped 'im petition the devil and get 'im there. They knowed the devil would make 'im a warlock. But he didn't. The devil had to leave. The devil couldn't stand 'im. He was too mean. When you get so mean the devil can't stand you, that's about as mean as you can get. Ain't it?

"They say right off Slasher sold and pledged his soul to the devil. He promised to do whatever the devil wanted him to do in exchange for the devil helping him. But it must notta worked. The devil probably tricked him. He was never a warlock that anybody knows about. Really was too mean, I reckon. Just think. Having the devil as a guest in your house, and then the devil can't stand the heat there!"

Not so long after the devil's last visit, Slasher died. Violently. Whether the devil had anything to do with Slasher's death is unknown, but there is speculation. Could it have been an accident? Suicide? Probably a homicide? Most people believe the insanely evil old man had some help dying.

Maybe the devil did help him in one last act.

They found Slasher impaled on the sharp spikes of the old time harrow in the hallway of the barn. Shaped like an arrowhead, the harrow had been turned bottom side up with the sharp-pointed metal ends of the spikes pointed upward. Apparently falling from the barn loft, Slasher's body hit the spikes face up and horizontally. Some spikes jabbed more than halfway through his body, one through the back of his head, two through his neck, one into his stomach, several more into other parts of his body. Death had frozen an expression of surprise and fear on his face—open mouth, intensely staring eyes.

They buried him that way.

Neighbor men came to help, but the sons of the deceased would not permit them to move the body. They dug the grave on the opposite side of the yard from their mother. They dug it extra deep, deep enough to hold the entire harrow edgewise with the body still impaled upon it. Around it and on top they hand-placed all the scrap iron and metal they could find—old tin, pipe, iron bars, buggy axles, wagon wheel hubs, harness chains, plow shovels, buckets, and an anvil. They finished filling the grave with dirt, packed it, then stacked heavy logs, crisscrossed, over it.

The old-timer nods his head. "They didn't want to take any chance of 'im coming back up out of that hole and bothering 'em again."

The children soon vacated their old homeplace, and none of them ever came back again.

The top-heavy grave of Mordecia Slasher held his body on into eternity. But not his ghost. His ghost just had to emerge and plunder around and annoy people, but with restrictions. Maybe the devil saw to that. While the ghost could be seen and heard, he could not touch you or cause any physical disturbance or damage. This restriction agitated the ghost and intensified his vehemence.

As long as the old homeplace existed, folks said that if you ventured close enough you could hear a variety of ghosts around the premises. Even after the homeplace was bulldozed, cleaned, cultivated and cropped, you could still hear the ghosts, more lonely now and less visible. Evening breezes and the promise of gilded moonlight brought a more plaintive rendition.

Always the snarling voice of Mordecia Slasher dominated. It enticed you closer, commanded you, cursed you, punctuated by the snap of a whip or the slap of a board against a human or animal body, and the accompanying wailing and pleading for the torture to stop.

Nearby, perhaps on the other side of where the yard used to be, comes a tired, agonized feminine voice warning people away, warning them not to be taken in by the monstrous male ghost. This ghostly voice captivates you by its sincerity, its earnestness, and its urgency. It alternately sobs and laments, then shrieks out in an uncontrollable expression of hopelessness and misery.

In between come juvenile voices begging their tormentor to stop.

One other ghostly voice has been identified as that of an elderly slave woman who keeps pleading over and over, "Please, mister master, don't beat me no mo'!"

On nights when ghosts prowl through these hills, folks claim you can see the inquisitive spirit of Mordecia Slasher, gliding along, peering, searching, as if expecting the devil to appear and help him. Others say you can see a bloody body impaled on sharp spikes. While these ghosts can't harm you, they can scare you to pieces. Maybe it's time they were laid to rest.

There's only one way to pacify the ghost of Mordecia Slasher, and hopefully, to satisfy or at least subdue the other ghosts.

If you know anything about how to become a warlock, start cruising through the Uwharries at night. This ghost will communicate.

THE SHAKING GHOST

Tycoon Floree didn't think much about the noise the first time he heard it. Neither did his neighbor, Fuddledee Skeeter, or Fudd's rangy son, Lindell, the latter a strapping mid-teenager who liked to brag that he wasn't scared of nuttin' and never would be. That's why the older men wanted Lindell along on their coon-hunting jaunts into the wild Uwharrie woods. If they encountered anything alarming or unsettling, Lindell would wade into it like a leaping tiger and find out what was going on. And in the Uwharries, mysterious noises, lights, and unsettling experiences are commonplace.

This noise sounded like leaves and limbs rustling and shaking high up in a nearby tree. Then a pattering into the dry leaves on the ground.

Deep in a strange part of the woods on this chilly, late September night, the three coon hunters had paused for a brief respite while their two dogs, ol' Rover and the almost-grown pup, Musket, scouted a quarter-mile radius around them to pick up a fresh coon track. They sat cross-legged in the dry leaves. Their lantern, on the end of a log in front of them, generated a welcome patch of illumination out of the blackness enveloping them. Every minute or two, ol' Rover bayed plaintively just to let them know he was still on the job.

The noise came again—a rustling, shaking, jostling sound—as if a person was high in a tree, shaking each branch vigorously.

Or stomping on each branch.

"Must be the wind up in the treetops," Ty speculated.

"Yeah, but there ain't no wind tonight," Fudd pointed out. "Not even a breeze, not even a leaf fluttering. That's why we picked tonight to hunt, remember? No wind."

They listened carefully. No wind noise at all. Only an encouraging long bay from ol' Rover.

Then the shaking noise came again. Plainly. At intervals, it sounded several more times. Just like an individual shaking a branch, except when he kicked it.

"Gimmie the flashlight," Lindell demanded. "I'll find out what it is."

While the men waited in the lantern light, Lindell located the tree, a large, stately shagbark hickory, which soared out of sight toward the stars. He maneuvered around it strategically, shining the five-celled flashlight into its canopy, but the light proved puny and futile. He muttered in disgust, stamping his feet in the brittle leaves.

That must have been a signal. A series of branch-shaking noises ascended into the upper part of the tree. Then a kick or two.

Lindell heard nuts falling off the tree and pattering into the dry leaves. In fact, one ricocheted off his shoulder. He circled the tree, light shining upward, his eyes straining. Nothing. The noise stopped.

He scrambled back into the lantern light. "Nuttin'," he reported. "Can't see too good. Too many leaves still hanging up there."

"We heard it plain," Ty said. "Creepy. Sounded like nuts falling down and hitting the leaves. Scalybark nuts are the best kind. We'll have to come back in daylight and pick 'em up."

"I'm gonna climb that tree," Lindell declared. "All the way to the top. I'll take this light with me. Then, from up there, I can see who's doing that shaking stuff."

"But a shagbark is hard to climb," his father cautioned. "That bark is tough, tough. It'll cut your arms and legs to pieces. It slips off in sheets, too, and might make you fall. Must be sixty, seventy feet up there."

"I'm wearing my overalls, my brogans, and long sleeves," Lindell said. "I can take it. I gotta see what's up there. You fellas watch on opposite sides of the tree. If you hear or see anything hit the ground or swing off into another tree, tell me."

With the flashlight in his pocket, Lindell shinnied up the big tree despite its ferocious bark. He got past the first branches, paused a moment, and continued. He found a limb where he could sit and rest a bit. A noise commenced way above his head. He whipped out his flashlight and splayed it around. Nothing. Still too many branches and leaves obstructing.

He climbed into the topmost branches.

There he saw something.

Above his head, a hammer-handle-sized branch shook vigorously, as if a stout person gripped it and shook with all his might.

Lindell rose as high as possible and swung his flashlight into the area where a person logically would have been.

"If a person had been there, I woulda hit 'im," he said later. "My flashlight went right through the spot. I swung so hard I lost my balance. I nearly fell outta that tree!"

The men below suggested that he go ahead and shake more nuts loose while he was in a good position to do so.

"We shook 'em all off," Lindell said, emphasizing the "we". "Every time I shook a limb, he—er, it would shake one, too. Just as hard as me, or harder. He was determined to do his part and then some. So, on toward the last, I just let 'im do all the shaking. When we got 'em all shook, everything was quiet again. Peaceful, back to normal. Never did see 'im or feel 'im, just seen them limbs a-shaking. But man, he was a good shaker!"

Lindell's story circulated through the Uwharries. Other coon hunters paused under nut-laden shagbark trees and experienced somewhat similar results. Not many volunteers would climb the tree like Lindell did, however. Then they discovered that you didn't have to be a coon hunter. Nor did you have to go at night. Just find yourself a magnificent shagbark loaded with ripe nuts. Stand under it and try to get the nuts to shower down.

Here's where the trouble came in.

Nobody could perfect just the right combination to make the ghost start shaking the limbs. They tried making shuffling noises with their feet in the dry leaves. Sometimes this worked. They cut small branches off saplings and flailed these into the dry leaves, making even greater noise. Sometimes it worked. They stood under the tree and shouted upward: "We're ready. Shake us off some nuts." Sometimes it worked.

But not always. Not even with "please".

Then again, sometimes the nuts would shake off the tree without any prompting.

Frustrating.

Lindell thought about it a lot. There had to be some explanation. What kind of ghost would shake nuts off of a shagbark? Year after year? He began researching and talking to people, especially older people. Finally—Lindell was a middle-aged man by now—he located a grizzled oldster in his nineties who recalled fragments of a story they pieced together.

"Yeah, I got it to work for me some back in my younger days," he remembered. "Worked good. You don't climb shags. You jest wait fer the nuts to fall. Or let it do the work for you. It will. It wants to. It's ready. But you gotta know how to start it if you want it to work at a certain time."

How do you start it at that certain time?

"Why, you jest call it by its name, that's how."

What's its name? What's its name?

"Well, let me see—I dunno—uh—I'll think of it in a minute—"

While he thought of the name, he told Lindell what he remembered of the rest of the story, all of it handed down from his forebears and their contemporaries.

Years before the Civil War, a prosperous Uwharrie farmer name of Bojures, or something like that, purchased an intact family of slaves—man, woman, and two children. Plus the family pet. A special pet. Very special. They lived in a cabin near the main house and helped with the farm and house work.

Why ol' man Bojures let the slave family keep the pet, nobody knows. Or even how it survived coming over on the slave ship or getting on in here to the Uwharries. But it did. He said lots of people saw it and watched it perform its special trick.

"What it was, was one of them big African monkeys," the old man said. "A big 'un. Like a baboon or a chimp or an ape or a young dwarf gorilla or something like that. One of 'em. They kept it tied part of the time. Let it loose like a guard dog at night around the house. Never was any prowlers around there, neither.

"But in the fall, when the shagbarks was heavy with nuts, that's when he'd go into action. He shinnied up that tough-barked tree in a second or two. Started with the low limbs and went on up to the very tiptop. Shake each one, whiplash it, like he was gonna break it. He didn't miss a limb. He shook bushels of nuts off big ol' high trees. Poured down like rain. They had 'im trained well. He knew his job. He did it. Lots of people come to watch. My granddaddy was among 'em."

There was some talk of Bojures renting out the slave family's pet baboon to other nut gatherers.

Anyway, the unusual pet's unusual career ended one day when a hunter mistook the baboon for a big coon or bobcat and shot it dead. The body lodged in the topmost branches of a huge shagbark tree, the carcass remaining there for weeks while the buzzards feasted.

"And the ghost of that baboon has been shaking nuts out of shagbark trees ever since," Lindell concluded. "He died up high in a shagbark. So that's where the ghost thinks he belongs. He enjoyed doing that so much alive, now his ghost is keeping on."

The pet's name? And now the ghost's name?

Lindell learned it from the old man, but he never would talk about it much or share the name.

One thing became special about Lindell. He was known in latter life as the "Scalybark man". In and around the Uwharries, nuts from shagbark trees are called "scalybarks". In his last few years, Lindell gathered tons of scalybarks. He sold them to individuals, stores, road-side produce stands, and specialty shops by the bucketful, tubful, sackful, or by the pickup truck load. Nobody could touch him when it came to lugging loads of scalybarks out of the Uwharrie woods.

Folks said, "He sure had a knack for nuts."

A knack, yes. But he also learned how to harness the special ability of a special ghost. He learned to call the ghost by its name. He didn't tell anyone about the name until shortly before he died. Today you can still find many magnificent shagbark hickory trees in the Uwharries. Many of them produce heavy crops of nuts in season.

Lindell had a friend, a veteran tree lover, who commented:

"The shagbark is a beautiful, unique tree. A mature tree can produce bushels of nuts. And they're delicious, but hard to get to. Shagbarks are not made for humans to climb. The bark hangs in slippery sheets and it's so tough it quickly dulls a chainsaw blade. Maybe nature designed these nuts just for the squirrels and animals. So if humans want them—there's some irony here—maybe nature has produced a ghost to help humans. Just here in this locality. Experimental? Will there be others? I'm not saying he will help you recover nuts even part of the time or ever. But he probably won't hurt you, either. Might be worth a try."

Go stand under one and see if the shaking ghost will favor you with a shower of nuts after you hear some rustling high in the foliage.

If not, try another tactic. The name. Lindell said the old man finally remembered the pet's name, and now the ghost's name—"Babbi," short for baboon, as in "Babbi, the Bojure's pet baboon."

So when you stand under the loaded tree and raise your upward voice to a shout, see if this works:

"Babbi. We're ready. Shake us off some nuts, Babbi. Please, Babbi."

THE NECKLACES

Everybody knew Rolleni Morrill was dying. After all, they had been expecting it for years. Her parents and family members knew it. Her friends and contemporaries knew it. Her preacher, business people, and adults knew it. The county doctor had told them years ago when she was a child that she had a congenital heart defect and that she wouldn't live much, if any, beyond her teen years. Now at age twenty-two, her borrowed time was about up.

Tall and too thin, Rolleni had a bony frame and face. Her eyes were sunken and her skin bluish. Her voice diminished to a whisper. She could hardly walk anymore and most of her outings were by wheelchair. But she smiled a lot, beamed when spoken to, and she loved to meet and greet people.

Practically everyone in this small town on the edge of the Uwharries knew Rolleni, and she knew them. All were impressed by her courage, her stamina, and her fight against this consuming disease that no doctor knew how to control back then.

The townspeople were impressed by something else, too.

Almost anytime you saw Rolleni, she would be wearing around her neck two big, thick necklaces, which gleamed and glinted brilliantly in the light. Her clothing obscured some of the heavy part of the necklaces, but the visible portion brought admiring gasps from the women. Rumors said the necklaces, resplendent with gold, diamonds, and gems, were worth a fortune and had been handed down to Rolleni by her great-great-grandmother, who brought them when she came over from the old country many generations ago. There had to be some nobility attached to the necklaces. Perhaps some of Europe's finest. The Morrill family still rated among the wealthiest in the area.

Rolleni died one morning in the fall. On the same day, they held her funeral early in the afternoon and buried her late in the afternoon in the ridgetop cemetery off the main road on the outskirts of town.

Two of the town's male teenagers, Ralph Bias and Scooper Mertz, were profoundly interested in the goings-on.

Along with most of the other townspeople, they expressed their condolence to the Morrill family. They went to the funeral and viewed the body while it lay in state in the church. They watched carefully and followed as the casket was closed, left the church, arrived in the cemetery, and was lowered into the grave and covered with clods and flowers.

"Eleven-thirty," Ralph whispered to Scooper. "Meet back here at eleven-thirty tonight."

They met a little after eleven-thirty and approached the cemetery from the backside. Ralph held a shovel in his hands, Scooper a flashlight and crowbar.

To be sure no one else lurked about on this chilly, blustery night, they circled through the cemetery with watchful eyes. In the faint starlight, shrubs loomed like monsters amid the tombstones. The breeze sang a mournful dirge overhead in the foliage of the few trees. A hoot owl flapped off his perch, scolding the boys for this intrusion. Panicked, the boys clutched each other for a moment. Ralph dropped the shovel on his foot and moaned in pain. Scooper cautioned him with a finger over his lips. "Quiet! We gotta hurry and get outta here," he hissed.

At the new grave, they removed the flowers, scraped off the mound, and began excavating, concentrating on the head end of the casket, which they remembered from hours earlier. Their shovel bumped on top of the casket. Ralph finished scraping away the dirt.

"Hand me the crowbar," he instructed Scooper.

With the tool, he pried open the upper half of the casket lid, revealing the head and shoulders of the corpse.

Already in the starlight, he could see tiny glints and sparkles from the necklaces around the corpse's neck. His right hand reached slowly toward those necklaces.

But–

Those necklaces started coming toward him.

His heart stopped. A squall of terror formed in his throat.

The corpse was struggling to sit up!

Scooper leaned closer to see if he could believe his eyes.

Then Rolleni pulled herself upright, gasping, breathing hard, her hands rubbing her face and eyes.

Both boys screamed and ran wildly off into the night, hoping Rolleni had not recognized them.

With no one to help, Rolleni had difficulty extricating herself from the casket and grave. Finally she crawled out, only to face another daunting task–getting home unaided. Half walking, half crawling, she managed the downhill slope to the edge of town. Then she struggled on, clutching walls, buildings, poles and fences until, exhausted, she fell against the door of her own home, crying weakly to be let inside.

It took a lot of pounding and pleading before the startled Morrill family opened the door and, disbelievingly, received their family member alive and back from the grave.

Nearby houses lit up. Soon the news had spread and half the townspeople came to see if this miracle was genuine. Many went to the cemetery to see for themselves if the grave had been opened.

Next day practically everyone in the area came to view the empty grave, which had liberated a comatose woman.

The aged constable poked around and confiscated the shovel, flashlight, and crowbar, hoping he could determine the owner. He never did.

Speculation was rife for days and weeks. And forever after.

Who opened the grave? And why?

Getting out by herself was an impossibility. Did Rolleni suddenly awaken from her comatose state, realize her condition, cry out for help, and someone heard her and dug her out? No one could have heard her cries from the underground casket. Even so, it would have caused a general alarm for help in getting her out and back home.

The valuable necklaces buried with her? Grave robbers after the necklaces? This became the most plausible and accepted theory. The noise of opening the casket and the inrush of cold air jerked the comatose woman back to consciousness, caused her to sit up, which panicked away the grave robbers, who dared not stay and help lest their true motive become known.

But who? Who would have done such a thing?

The perpetrators had criminal intent. Yet, they saved a life—would they be prosecuted?

Rolleni Morrill recovered amazingly fast. The old country doctor checked her every day for a while, shaking his head at the miracle. Her skin color returned to normal. All her vital signs remained good. She gained weight, strength, energy, and a remarkable zest for living. She married, had four children, and became such a passionate volunteer in her church, school, and community that everybody loved her.

She lived for another forty years.

At social functions she wore the two thick, heavy necklaces—necklaces of a brilliance that no other ornament could match.

Ralph and Scooper grew up and never left the community. They finished school, got some college training, married, had families, went into business pursuits, and became solid citizens. Never was there a hint of anything shady or suspicious in their background.

Whenever they encountered Rolleni at community functions, they smiled greetings to each other, made small talk, but never engaged in any prolonged discussion. Once in a great while there appeared to be a bit of intrigue in her smile. Otherwise she was very discreet in her behavior around them.

After forty years passed, Rolleni became sick again. She grew critically ill. Specialists examined her. All pertinent tests and treatments were given. All the medical people shook their heads. It was terminal. She would die soon. She mandated no vegetable type existence. She was ready.

Rolleni died on a Monday. After the funeral on Wednesday afternoon, they buried her in the same grave in the ridgetop cemetery from which she had escaped over forty years earlier.

Some people remarked about the absence of the necklaces on the corpse. Folks wondered and talked.

There were superstitions about using the same grave over again. Bad luck? Conflict? Would it generate ghosts? Would anyone guard this grave at night?

On Friday Ralph and Scooper each received an identical bulky security envelope, hand delivered by a special courier. No return address.

Each envelope contained a beautiful, thick and heavy necklace brilliantly studded with gold, diamonds, and precious gemstones.

Also each envelope contained an unsigned note which read:

SORRY YOU HAD TO WAIT SO LONG
THANKS FOR WHAT YOU DID

If you know where to look in the Uwharries, folks claim you can see ghosts flitting around a certain grave in a little ridgetop cemetery–a grave which received two bodies, but got to keep only one.

It had to wait a long time, too.

OL' RATTLE

Cleatus Oglethorpe gathered random pieces of firewood around the edge of his yard to build a fire under the washpot to boil a week's accumulation of dirty clothes. Always he helped his wife get the washing started by building a fire to get the water boiling. On this fine spring morning, the chipper oldster looked for dead wood and a pine knot or two to get the fire rolling in a hurry. He knew he had left a pine knot behind a big stump.

"I started to reach around the stump," he said later, "when something clamped my arm and wouldn't let it move forwards anymore. Jest froze it right there. I tried to unfreeze it and push it on, but I couldn't. Then I tried pulling my hand backwards and it worked. I could draw it back. Then I walked around the stump and there, right beside that pine knot, lay a big copperhead, coiled up, his head up, his tongue flicking out, ready to strike.

"If I had put my hand on up close to that pine knot, that copperhead woulda bit me shore as the world. Big as he was, that pizen woulda kilt me before anybody coulda done anything to help. Yes, 'er, that was a close 'un.

"Yeah, ol' Rattle did it. I know it was him. I been thankin' him ever since. Yeah, it was ol' Rattle."

Ol' Rattle?

He is a ghost with a specialized mission—warning people, mostly Uwharrie people, about hazards. Mostly outdoor hazards, too. A lot of these involve poisonous snakes. Ol' Rattle has been warning folks for a century or two. Only hand-me-down versions exist of his early exploits. Older Uwharrians believe ol' Rattle is still on the job, although today's modern, fast-living people don't give him credit anymore.

And this rankles the ghost.

If nobody believes in him anymore, maybe he'll just stop his ministrations altogether. After generations of helping people, he needs a rest anyway.

Legend credits two brothers with creating this ghost.

One fall morning, they were out in a wild part of the Uwharries with their long-barreled muskets, hunting wild turkey and deer to stock up their meat supply for the coming winter. Crossing a creek, they blundered into a nest of rattlesnakes and both got bitten, multiple times, on the hands and face as they tried to help each other during a frenzied scrambling around. Unsure of what to do to counteract the rattler venom, they weakened and died there amongst the reptiles.

Before the second brother died, he was able to communicate with another hunter, an old man who lived in the area, who was out hunting and heard the commotion. The old man came to see if he could help. He held the brother's head on his leg and tried to comfort him, but it was too late.

The dying man looked at the body of his brother. Tears spilled out of glazed eyes. Blood sputtered out the corner of his mouth. His voice wavered.

"Nobody warned us–we don't wanna die–I'm coming back–back to warn people–about this–"

He coughed and died.

And he did come back.

"About dusk," one Uwharrie resident said, "I went out to the woodshed to get an armful of dry pine wood to use in the cookstove when something stopped me right at the entrance. Something solid. Like an invisible door or fence or pole. Couldn't budge it. I couldn't see good in the woodshed. I stepped back, got my ol' oil lantern off the corner, struck a match and lit it and turned back toward the shack again. There lay two big rattlesnakes. One was crawling off. But the other one was coiled and ready. If I had stooped down and started loading stove wood over my arm like I usually do, whooo-eee, them snakes, probably both of 'em, woulda bit me shore 'nuff. It was the ghost of that dead rattler-bit man. He come back to warn me. He said he would. He shore did."

And he did for lots of others, too.

Warning about the presence of poisonous snakes accounted for most of his interventions. But not all.

Some recipients reported that they thought they heard a faint rattling noise, not unlike the angry buzzing of a rattlesnake's rattlers, which accompanied the warning. This rattling noise is what gave the ghost his name. Grateful people, who escaped harm, began calling him "ol' Rattle." The name stuck and was used whether or not the noise was heard.

One deer hunter said he pointed his rifle at a clump of bushes where he thought a big buck was hiding. He took careful aim and started pressing gently on the trigger, but the trigger froze and would not move. A second or two later, out of the bushes walked another deer hunter wearing camouflaged clothing. "He saved me from killing a man," the grateful hunter said. Afterward his trigger worked perfectly.

Terboat McIver and a friend were walking along the railroad tracks on a chilly moonlit night. Both had taken a nip or two from a pint of moonshine. Suddenly they heard the freight train rumbling toward them, and saw its big headlight bearing down. They tried to jump out of the way. The friend made it, but Terboat stumbled and fell because his foot had gotten trapped in the track. He said the light and chugging engine appeared to be just inches from him.

"I knew I was a goner. I could just feel death all around me. But that freight train stopped suddenly. I mean *suddenly*. Just inches from me. I got my foot loose and flung myself back outta the way. An' that train started up again and went on just like it had never stopped. Now I'm here to tell yuh, a freight train making forty miles an hour don't just stop suddenly. No way. And when it starts up again, it don't just suddenly start traveling at forty miles per hour. No way. But that one did. It saved my life."

A woodsman said he walked along a path through the woods one bright day about noon, when something invisible stopped him and held him fast. He couldn't move in any direction. He heard a rustling sound, and then watched a large dead tree slam down across the trail a few steps in front of him. Had he been walking normally, he would have been crushed to death under the falling tree.

A man fishing under a bluff on the bank of the Yadkin River reported a similar experience. He had dozed off when something woke him, caused him to stand, and move a few steps to one side. He looked back and saw his fishing pole. He decided to go retrieve it, but he couldn't move. Not an inch. A second later, he heard a thumping from above. Here came a boulder big as a washpot, which landed exactly where he had been sitting and dozing.

One bare-legged woman said something stopped and redirected her to avoid walking through a thick patch of poison ivy.

Three tenderfoot scouts got separated from their group and wandered off into a lonely part of the woods. As sundown approached, they panicked at the thought of spending the night lost and unprepared in the wild woods. Suddenly everything quieted. They sensed an unseen presence. It led them, single file, a mile through the woods until they recognized a familiar landmark and made their way back to camp.

There were other reports of narrow and seemingly miraculous escapes involving rock climbing, firewood cutting, vicious dogs, fishing and canoeing mishaps, near drownings, wood fires, snow storms, and lightning strikes. As well as many more snake warnings.

Years ago some vague reports surfaced about ol' Rattle taking on a new role, that of general preservationist and conservationist throughout the entire Uwharrie area. He would help Mother Nature and forest officials in such matters as timber cutting, pest and disease control, off-road vehicle damage, litter bugging, erosion, wildlife management, waterway pollution, and general safety for residents and visitors.

Is ol' Rattle still on the job?

Everyone hopes so, although reports of his interventions have subsided.

If you are outdoors in the beautiful Uwharries and hear a faint buzzing and rattling, stop whatever you're doing. Look around and listen carefully.

It could be ol' Rattle trying to get your attention.

PIRATE GHOSTS

Ghosts guarding buried treasure—often pirate treasure—are identified with many communities along navigable waterways with connections to the seacoast. The Uwharries contain at least one such spot, a fabulous subterranean treasure trove of booty from the high seas, hidden here almost three centuries ago and still guarded by as many as a dozen ill-tempered ghosts. None of them will let you get far in exploring the site.

Because if you persist, these ghosts might make you one of them.

It has happened before.

That's why the number of guardian ghosts keeps growing at this location.

It started with Bernard Matheson, who was born and reared on a pioneer farm near where the Uwharrie River joins the Yadkin to form the Pee Dee River, the latter flowing on to empty into the Atlantic Ocean near Georgetown, South Carolina. A strapping, muscled young man with an impressive physique by the age of fourteen, Bernard grew restless on the farm. He wanted to travel and see the world. He got permission to ride horseback to visit an uncle for a few weeks in the Fayetteville area. A reformed pirate, the uncle filled the lad with fanciful tales of adventure on the high seas, giving him names and tips in case he wanted to follow this activity when he got older. All the way back home, Bernard dreamed of flashing swords, roaring cannon, and chests of gold and silver aboard his pirate ship which pitched over rolling waves.

When he arrived home he found his family slaughtered, apparently by marauding Indians. The attackers had attempted to burn the home as well. Bernard buried the mutilated bodies of his father, mother, brother, and sister in a common grave. He piled rocks to mark the spot and discourage digging animals. Straight-away, he stuffed a few possessions in a sack, rigged up a small log craft, poled it out to midstream, and set adrift down the mighty Pee Dee.

Ten years later, a laden pirate ship made its way up the Pee Dee River as far as it could navigate safely, almost reaching the Uwharrie.

Bernard Matheson barked orders to his crew members. They moored
the ship in a little cove in the mouth of a creek. They unloaded tools
and cargo into smaller rowboats, then completed their journey into the
mouth of the Uwharrie River. There they made camp.

Ghosts may have become active at this point–ghosts of his slain
family members welcoming him back and urging him to greater goals.

More ghosts joined them before long.

Utilizing the labor of several slaves brought along for this specific
job, Bernard soon had a combination fort and residence under construction. Two of his trusted crew members supervised the work, since
Bernard spent a lot of time with a female captive taken in their plunder
on the high seas.

Along with the construction, the slaves had to dig a large hole in the
loamy earth near a big oak tree. Then they waterproofed with tar three
large chests containing gold, silver, coins, jewelry, small weapons, and
a variety of other booty. After lowering the chests into the hole, they
left it conspicuously uncovered until they finished the work on the
combination fort-house. Bernard, in a drunken orgy, ordered the slaves
beheaded and their bodies dumped in on top of the treasure. Soon
Bernard tired of his female companion, and turned her over to his two
henchmen. She died within a week. Her body joined those of the slaves
on top of the treasure. The pirates then filled in and disguised the big
hole.

At intervals of a few years, more pirate ships, ever bigger and always
carrying heavier loads of booty, made the trip up the Pee Dee. More
treasure–and more bodies–went into the loamy earth near the big oak.
Only Bernard and his few trusted henchmen returned to the sea.

Hunters and fisherman passing near the Uwharrie reported seeing
ghostly shapes and hearing mournful wailing. Few wanted to risk
camping nearby. A few brave souls attempted it, but were frightened
away. Nobody yet associated the location with buried treasure.

By this time Bernard had become one of the most dreaded pirates
off the east coast. His ruthlessness and ferocity made many enemies
among his kindred. Several countries encouraged privateers and naval
vessels to run him down and eliminate him. Some pursued him, but
couldn't locate his hiding places.

On his last trip up the Pee Dee, Bernard sailed the big pirate ship as
far as it could go, then anchored it in mid-river. They unloaded
everything of value, including two captive females, onto the smaller
rowboats. One keg of gunpowder stayed in the hold. Once clear of the
ship, they ignited the gunpowder, blowing the ship to smithereens. It

sank below the surface and left no evidence that a pirate ship had ever been in the vicinity.

This time when the slaves finished digging a new hole near the big oak tree for the treasure chests, the pirates threw the screaming laborers into a room-sized bog of quicksand discovered in a nearby marsh. Bernard and his two most trusted henchmen then forced the rest of their crew into the quicksand.

Trying to avoid the terrible marsh, the two females agreed to a plot hatched by the henchmen, Munrumy and DePaul. For a share of the treasure, the women promised to get Bernard drunk on rum and vulnerable for easy disposal.

Munrumy and DePaul lugged the passed-out drunken Bernard to the big oak, bound his hands and feet, then propped him erect and tied him to the trunk of the tree. They took turns running their swords through his body and slashing his neck to ribbons, until his head hung grotesquely to one side. Finally tiring of the sport, the men flung the bloody torso into the new hole on top of the treasure chests. They forced the women to help cover and camouflage the hole.

Within a day or two, the men tossed the battered women into the quicksand bog. They vanished quickly.

Now only two men remained who knew the location of the treasure—and the bodies.

Each filled a satchel with booty and crammed all he could carry into his pockets. Each drew a crude map of the location, and concealed the map in his clothing.

They shook hands and swore an oath to return in exactly five years, dig up all the treasure, divide it, and take it away.

During this interval, passers-by reported more ghosts. White shapes floated around in the gloom. Cries of distress could be heard day and night. A swashbuckling, gigantic pirate with a flashing sword dominated the reports. Most people in the sparsely settled area considered it a place to avoid.

When the five years ended, only DePaul showed up. Munrumy had been killed in a port city in a drunken brawl. DePaul had survived a run-in with pursuers, some of whom might have followed him up the Pee Dee. He brought with him in the big rowboat a towering black man named Bowser to help with the rowing and digging. Very superstitious and edgy, Bowser could sense unseen entities around the place, which kept him apprehensive and always looking over his shoulder. He begged DePaul to hurry and get away from this spooky place.

Since the fort-residence and all its contents had burned to the ground during his absence, DePaul lounged around the campfire with his jittery helper. Bowser kept a big sword at his side to fight off the spooks. DePaul indulged in rum and kept his musket handy. Wails of departed souls drifted in the night air. Mysterious noises would not let them rest.

Suddenly a bright light shined on them. Someone had removed a shield from a lighted lantern. An authoritative voice boomed:

"Don't move! Hold still or you will be shot. You are now prisoners of the British Navy."

Bowser jumped up and swung his big sword toward the light. A shot roared from a flash of fire. Bowser staggered, then crashed to the ground, dying.

DePaul grabbed his musket and fired at a shadowy figure, which gasped and crumpled.

"Nobody's taking me prisoner," he shouted.

A pistol shot fired at close range struck DePaul in the middle of the chest. Mortally wounded, he sprawled to his knees, then fell prostrate, struggling for breath. His ragged gasping continued until dawn when he died.

At daylight the young naval officer surveyed the three bodies, including that of his mate, a junior officer. He retrieved a few personal items from the bodies and stored these in a bag in his rowboat to take back with him. The bodies of DePaul and Bowser, he drug into the river for disposal. The body of his mate went into a shallow grave he dug right over the treasure trove. He pounded a crude cross into place there.

Ready to drift downstream, he untied his rowboat, but spotted someone a short distance away through the trees. It was the figure of an attractive female, scantily clad, who motioned him thither. Intrigued, he started toward her. She receded a few steps, but beckoned him on. He stepped across the corner of the bog, but his footing gave way, plunging him into the quicksand, which swallowed him within a moment or two.

Next day, due to heavy rain upstream, the river swelled and swept away the rowboats, the new grave marker, and all signs of recent occupancy. As the decades passed, the location returned to the primordiality of centuries past.

But a new era dawned. More settlers arrived, coming down from the northern states, and upriver from the coast. Farms were carved out of the wilderness. Rough roads pushed through. Ferries spanned the rivers. A steady flow of entrepreneurs came—hunters, trappers, fishermen, timber cutters, gold miners, developers, business-minded vision-aries–all recognizing the potential.

The ghosts around the mouth of the Uwharrie had a field day at this influx.

Long dormant, they reveled at this opportunity to re-activate and scare visitors all up and down the river. They've been doing it ever since. In fact, their activity increases as more and more treasure hunters learn the story about the pirate treasure, and bring ever more sophisti-cated detection devices in their quest to liberate it. The ghosts monitor all visitors. They tolerate and amuse themselves with the innocent, recreational, just-looking-around boaters, fishermen, campers, hikers, and assorted adventurers. But if you become too insistent in looking for the treasure, they hustle you off the property–or worse.

The ghosts won't permit the treasure to be found or removed. Doing so might jeopardize their own existence here. So the ghosts aren't leaving. Never. They like this location. They like this spectral commu-nity they have established, probably one of the largest ghostly concen-trations in the state. They enjoy the seclusion, the variety of personalities among their number, and the excellent prospects for expanding their colony's population. They remain eager, even vigilant, for new induc-tees.

One man started digging near where he assumed the old oak tree once stood.

"I must have been at the right spot, too," he said. "Something drove me away. It would have made anybody leave. It had to be the ghosts."

After the first few licks, each excavating tool he used started striking his feet. The pointed end of the pick punctured the end of his shoe, injuring two toes. The long-bladed shovel hit the edge of his shoe bottom, ripping off a portion of the sole. Next he tried his "persuader", a tall metal bar with a chisel-sharp end. A mighty downward swing sent it into the top of his shoe, down beside his instep and out through the bottom, resulting in a badly sprained ankle. All the tool thrusts started in a controlled manner, but were redirected to the feet by the ghosts.

Another digger said his pick froze in midair and wouldn't budge until he stepped back a few paces. Then it fell at his feet. All other tools did likewise.

On several occasions two men brought a gasoline-powered hole digger with shaft extensions, since they were determined to sink deep holes until they hit the treasure. But their engine never started. If they hung around, the engine began smoking and melting as if a giant magnifying glass focused a sun bead on it.

Detection devices and instruments worked at first, but then became incapacitated, along with their operators.

Nighttime seekers, even campers, don't last long. A gun muzzle belches fire and a bullet whizzes past your head. Flashing broadswords slice through the murkiness, their ominous thrusts coming ever closer to each individual present. Feet become tangled in rope, and if you are not clever in extricating yourself, you will be dragged toward the river or toward a faintly illuminated eerie opening in the trees, from which come mournful lamentations.

Day or night, visitors claim you can hear the anguished wailing of the beheaded slaves. Also the desperate gasping for breath from the dying DePaul. Or the slobbering grunts from Bernard the pirate as the swords drive through his body. Occasionally the authoritative voice of the naval officer will question your presence.

On misty nights boaters may glimpse the outline of a big pirate ship. If the wind is right, the image may be accompanied by the voice of rum-ravaged Bernard the pirate, barking orders to his crew. Should this creaky pirate ship try to run your boat down, just close your eyes for an instant.

When the water level drops substantially, people go out relic hunting along the exposed shoreline. Once in a great while a person will pull an ornate piece of wood or metal out of the mud—an item completely foreign to this locality. Never in all their intrigue and wondering about its origin do they realize that it came from a pirate ship blown to bits in the middle of the river in pre-Revolutionary War days.

Younger men are warned about one vindictive ghost near the buried pirate treasure. This ghost's appetite for revenge and retaliation will never be satisfied. The more men she can lure into the quicksand to join her, the happier she becomes. The number of her victims appears to be growing. Because Bernard helps her. If the man hesitates when she beckons, the ghost of Bernard pushes him from behind. Since the ghost of crazy old Bernard no longer can distinguish male from female, this warning applies to both men and women.

If you loiter around this location and spot an attractive female, alluringly dressed, beckoning you from across a bog, please turn and run the opposite direction as fast as you can.

Unless you want to join the club.

THE HEAVY-FOOTED GHOST

Two youngsters, Pell Bakbee and Tubby Tafford, loved to heckle the old witch woman who shuffled along the country lane near their homes every day about dusk.

They called her an ugly old woman, and even worse names: "You look like a pile of dirty clothes a-walking toward the wash pot–ha, ha, ha." They kicked gravel in her face. They pelted her with acorns, corncobs, green persimmons, and even with spoiled fruits and vegetables. They made their hound dogs growl and bark at her heels. Once in a while, they hid behind a bush and dashed a pail of water over her pathetic figure, even in cold weather.

Occasionally other adolescents who manned heckling locations farther along the lane joined Pell and Tubby. Pestering the strange old woman became a favorite pastime for them.

Hardly any of the parents knew about the heckling. Those who had heard about it never realized its extent or how vicious it had become. Some of the parents harbored hostile feelings toward the old woman anyway, and the children used this attitude to justify their actions.

The old witch woman–most people called her Ol' Lady Fidora–took it in stride. She lifted scrawny hands and a heavy scarf to shield her face from the pelting, sometimes twisting her shoulders and shuffling sideways past the hecklers. She had to use this lane because it was the best way between the village and her shack at the edge of the woods. If the pelting attacks became too vicious, she would stop, turn, and stare at the boys. If the dogs nipped at her feet too sharply, she stopped, turned, and stared at them.

These stares were effective as well as memorable.

One of the hecklers, Tubby Tafford, talked about it all his life. He lived to be an old man, dying generations ago.

"You've had a person stare at you so hard that you stopped whatever you was doing," he said. "She did that. I could have my arm drawed back ready to throw, then I couldn't move it. None of us could throw or move our arms till she got outta range. Same with the dogs. She'd stare at them. They stopped. They would whimper, twist around addled and confused till she got outta sight."

Later, Ol' Lady Fidora used another technique to squelch her hecklers, a technique that impressed their parents, a technique that left ghostly repercussions and possible applications into the present day.

When the hecklers got together as a group, usually well after dark, they walked to the witch's isolated shack. There they used pebbles, green apples, hickory nuts, and other objects to pelt the walls of the shack and its tin roof. Also they disturbed the roosting chickens and punched the measly old goat with sticks until it baa-aa-aaed in pain.

This commotion brought the old woman outside, jerking a shawl over her nightgown, the white collar of which ruffled up around her head. Unable to see well, she held her big lighted lantern high, bobbing it around and peering into the darkness.

"Who's there? What do ye want?" her voice shrilled impatiently into the night.

Somebody in the group snickered. Then collective footsteps stampeded away.

"Them kids," she said wearily. "Them kids." She turned toward the fading footsteps and waved her lantern. "You young 'uns have gotta stop it. You hear? You gotta stop it."

She took a few steps forward, waving the lantern, and repeated her warning. Then she went back inside.

Tubby Tafford told what happened next:

"The second time we did that, just a few nights later—was a Saddity night I believe—is when it happened. Weren't but three of us this time, me an' Pell an' Tungsen Dippie. We didn't do much. Just rocked her roof a little. Made the chickens squawk and flap around. Whacked the ol' goat on the hine end till he baa-aaed a little. She barged out quick, waving that lantern and calling to us. We had no mind to answer. We'd heard about her black magic and casting spells and stuff. None of that fer us. But it happened anyway. She got us.

"She came closer and we tried to run, but we couldn't. Our feet was froze to the ground. Wouldn't budge. Like they was in a bucket of solid concrete. Couldn't move 'em at all. Heavy as lead. Felt like they were swollen. Pell an' Tung were the same way. All three of us. She had us. Horrible feeling when you can't pick up your feet. Neither one.

"Well, she came up close. Took 'er time. She held that lantern up close to our faces and looked at us good. She recognized us. Yep. She knowed who we was and where we lived. She knowed we had been pestering her for a long time. She coulda kilt us right then and there. Or let them big dogs of hers chew us to pieces. But she didn't. She warned us instead. She said we had to quit bothering her. All of us.

And she meant it. If we didn't stop bothering her, we'd have more heavy feet. Heavier and heavier. All of us. That if we even thought about bothering her again, our feet would be heavy as anvils and stay that way till the thought left our minds.

"She said she was going back to her shack. When she reached her door, our feet would free up. And we better use them, too, for she would set the two dogs loose on us. No racehorse coulda caught us on that run back home—just ahead of them dogs, too. We slammed into the door, woke up the family, and had to tell our parents what happened. Next day several pops and moms had a talk with the old woman. They come back and told us if we ever bothered Ol' Lady Fidora again they would skin us alive. We didn't, either, but some of the other kids did."

The other kids refused to believe about the heavy feet, so they had to find out for themselves. The same thing happened to them on a nocturnal pelting visit to the witch's home. She came out waving her lantern and accosted them. They tried to run, but couldn't. Their feet were immobilized and stayed that way until she freed them, whereupon they scrambled madly for home, with the huge black dogs snapping at their heels.

That stopped most of the pestering. The younger kids and the non-believers found out the hard way. If they threw anything or jeered at the old woman, their feet swelled and felt heavy as lead, leaving them immobilized until she saw fit to release them. Such experiences convinced the perpetrators to leave the witch alone.

"Ol' Lady Fidora was a good witch," Tubby remembered. "Us kids didn't know it back then, but we learned it later. She helped people. She could help sick people get well. She could take away hexes and evil spells cast by other witches. She could make your milk cow give more milk, your hens lay more eggs, your hogs grow fatter, your garden do better, even make rain come. All of us felt mighty bad about bothering her when we was young 'uns."

After she died, the witch woman continued ministering to the community.

Rather, her ghost did. Again, in a heavy-footed way.

According to the stories Tubby Tafford left his descendants, Ol' Lady Fidora's influence was felt as a disciplinarian, sort of a blanket conscience of the community. Practically everyone, young and old, felt it plainly—to the point that crime and mischief in the community became almost unheard of.

Anytime anyone in the community *thought* about doing anything wrong, their feet began to grow heavy. If they persisted in such negative thinking, their feet immobilized them until they re-directed their mindset toward the positive. Then the heaviness let up. Always accompanying the heavy feet was the mental picture of the old witch woman holding high her lantern and bobbing it around in the murkiness.

Tubby said, "I 'sperienced it. Pell and Tung and everybody else did. Plain and simple. If you even thought about doing something bad or mean, your feet started getting heavy and stayed that way till you got it outta your mind. If you went ahead real quick and tried to do something mean without thinking about it, you couldn't. Your feet froze. You couldn't take a step. I 'sperienced it. An' always in your mind you saw that ol' woman waving her lantern about. Real plain image. You could see her and that light with your eyes open or closed. Everybody did. You didn't get heavy feet without experiencing that light, too.

"Best thing ever happened in our little community. No killing. No brawling or fighting, nobody mad at their neighbor, no stealing, nobody jealous or lusting, no cheating or slacking, no family disputes or abuse, no mischief or property damage, no heavy drinking or drugging, nobody lying or spreading false rumors. Lots of harmony and trust. Nobody locked their doors. Nobody afraid of nobody else. Hardly anybody ever sick or hurt. Just about perfect back then. Yep, I lived through some of it.

"Funniest damn things happen. Scared plenty of people silly. Even the preacher, even the school teacher. Everybody got heavy feet more than once. Some a lot, lot more. Didn't matter where you was, either. You could be in the middle of the road, halfway up or down the steps, a-singing in the choir, riding horseback or in the buggy, floating down the creek in a canoe, picnicking, even dreaming I guess. When that bad stuff started in your mind, *wham*! Your feet got so heavy you couldn't budge and stayed that way till some goodness flooded back into you. You always looked around to see who was watching. Everybody knowed what it was, because it had happened to them. Them bobbing lantern lights always come in your mind and that image stayed with you till after your feet freed up. Yeah, yeah, it happened to me, too, to these big feet right here under me, but I ain't telling no more 'bout that."

Folks wonder if big-footed people in the Uwharries today could be descended from the individuals who experienced the heavy-footed ghost firsthand.

They wonder, too, if some of the mysterious lights often seen bobbing around in the Uwharrie woods could be the lantern held high by the ghost of Ol' Lady Fidora, still warning people to leave her alone.

And still reminding people to think positively.

NATTIE'S GHOST

Like most spirits, Nattie's ghost only appears at certain times and under certain circumstances. His ghosting specialty has never been duplicated as far as anyone knows. It took a long while, but people in his native Uwharrie community learned how to recognize this apparition, almost predict his arrival, and exercise some control of his actions. Once the locals learned his routine, they were able to thwart some of his nefarious activities. Ghosts don't like to be thwarted. That's why Nattie's ghost moves around to a new community every few decades, so he can ply his trade without interference. There are lots of new communities left in the Uwharries for him to travel to and practice in before he starts back around.

His specialty is assisted suicide.

For a century or two before today's doctors put a label on it, Nattie's ghost practiced euthanasia, or mercy killing. He's good at it. He knows all the best and easiest methods. He knows exactly how, when, where, and how long it will take. And he is eager not only to share this expertise, but to actively assist anyone in carrying out this act, either impulsively or as a premeditated act. All it takes is for you to get this idea in your consciousness, and then presto! he's there like an ever-present mentor. With missionary zeal, Nattie doesn't let up until he welcomes you to the other side.

Most of the time nobody knows he's present until it's too late.

In rare instances when he is detected and thwarted, he's ready to move on to new territory anyhow.

His specialty-within-a-specialty becomes obvious occasionally—disguising his orchestrated deaths as accidents. He gloats over this sometimes.

Bacchus DeLany's death could have been either way. A handsome young man of nineteen, Bacchus learned that his girlfriend had gotten tired of waiting on him and run off and married his rival. His first thought was to get his gun and go shoot his rival. He rejected this thought, but another idea hit him. Kill himself. That would prove to everyone that he loved the girl so much he couldn't live without her.

More and more this thought motivated him. At the rural home of his Uncle Raphael, itinerant pastor of several backwoodsy churches, something directed Bacchus to a wire cage at the rear of a shed. A wire partition separated the two occupants of the cage–large, live rattlesnakes. His uncle used them in his snake-handling services. Bacchus watched as a ghostly hand unlatched the cage door and reached inside. A snake immediately attacked it. Then another ghostly hand opened the door to the other compartment and reached inside. Immediately the snake struck it.

Automatically Bacchus rolled up his sleeve. He stuck his hand into the cage and felt the fangs of the rattler puncture his wrist. Withdrawing it, he used the bitten hand to roll up his other sleeve. He thrust this arm into the other compartment with similar results. As he slumped to his knees in mounting pain, he saw the ghostly hand closing the doors to the cage.

Hours later, Raphael returned to find his nephew dead on the ground near the cage.

Raphael explained to everyone: "He was trying to help me. Practicing with them snakes. He wanted to handle them during my services at church. I was gonna let 'im do it later when he got a little more confident. Takes practice. Takes faith. Bacchus tried it before he was ready. I'm sorry for 'im–awful tragedy."

Scratch Pierson flung himself off the one-hundred-foot cliff on Pawley's Mountain and died on the rocks below. So everyone assumed. In reality, Nattie's ghost pushed him over. Scratch went there to end his life, but had about changed his mind when the ghost forced him over.

Jilted by her lover, Novella Deeter felt compelled to go to Lover's Leap looking for him. She peered over the edge and saw him, smiling with arms outstretched, waiting for her to jump into his arms. She did, but she ended her life in the gorge below. Nattie's ghost had deceived her.

The ghost caused Hilda Meecaps to overdose on drugs.

He caused Dinges Malone to stuff himself with rat poison.

He caused a lonely widower, Salberto Finninger, to pull the trigger of a shotgun with the end of the barrel in his mouth.

Nattie's ghost caused Parson McGeorge to row out to the middle of the lake, tie the anchor around his leg, and slip overboard.

In the case of a semi-invalid, Ross McIntine, the ghost did about everything because the victim wasn't physically able. The ghost helped Ross to the basement, sat him atop a stepladder, fashioned a noose around his neck, tied the rope tautly and securely to a joist overhead, then eased the ladder out from under him.

These and dozens more have been attributed to the ghost.

"About one a year—that seemed to be his goal," an oldster remembers. "At least one a year."

Many years and many such deaths passed before family members and investigators began to recognize the ghost's signature. One word—Kirk. Always that one word could be seen on or near the body of the assisted suicide victim. Sometimes it was smeared in bloody letters, scratched in dirt or sand, spelled out in gravels or acorns, etched into wood or metal, even spray-painted onto rocks, walls, posts, or tree trunks. It appeared that the ghost had to have the last word. And that word was Kirk.

But what was the significance of Kirk?

Nobody knew. It mystified them for years.

Finally an old man recalled a hand-me-down story about how Nattie became a ghost in the first place.

* * *

Old Nattie Watkins had lived a rough, tough life, and finally, in his eighties, he came to the end of his rope. He had raised a large family of children, farmed, hunted, prospected, drunk whiskey, ridiculed churches, and fussed at church people. About all that remained faithful to him now was his old mule, ol' Sam, who stood by him no matter where he fell on the trail in a drunken stupor and no matter how long he lay there. Grizzled and frail, Nattie lay on his deathbed surrounded by one son, Kirk, and a few neighbors and friends who had gathered to see him off on his last journey.

"I got a long way to go and a short time to get ready," Nattie said. He looked up at the familiar faces. "Kirk, I want you to go with me. It's a long way and the road is rough and muddy. I need you to help."

He looked at others. "Boys, git ol' Sam hitched up and ready 'cause it's about time. Ol' Sam'll stay with me."

To another man: "Go git my ol' gun and bring it here so I'll have it ready, too."

He rambled on: "Kirk, I want you to go with me. Won't ya?" Kirk, a middle-aged man, snarled negatively at his father and left the room. "I may hafta come back after that boy," the bedfast man said.

"Boys, git the lap robe and tuck it around me good to keep the wind and rain and mud off me and the cold out." They tucked the quilts down around him as if arranging the lap robe.

Again he asked Kirk to accompany him on this last journey. From the doorway, Kirk answered, "I ain't going with you anywhere, ever, ol' man."

Nattie looked at all the faces. "Is everything all ready, boys?"

"Yep, all is ready, Uncle Nat," they assured him.

On this cold winter day with wind moaning at the cabin's eaves, Uncle Nat wriggled his head deeper into his pillow, took a deep breath, sighed softly, and murmured, "Here I goes." He died within a moment or two. Absolutely painless with no sign of a struggle.

*   *   *

Uwharrians believe that Nattie had such a good success orchestrating his own death that his ghost took up the same activity with assisted suicides, which, by now, probably number in the hundreds. These deaths will continue, too, until the ghost finds Kirk. The ghost's obsession with Kirk accounts for this name being at the scene of all the deaths.

The trouble is, soon after his father's death, Kirk sold out everything here and moved to California where he lived until he died and was buried there a long, long time ago. This has confused the ghost, who is still looking for Kirk here.

The Uwharrians are looking for a volunteer. They want a healthy and agile middle-aged man to assume the identity of Kirk Watkins and fake a suicide, which Nattie's ghost orchestrates. He'll have to be an actor or stunt man to pull off the deal. Probably wear a nametag pinned on his shirt. To be convincing, he will need to practice the theatrics of dying.

No one knows just how strong the influence of Nattie's ghost is in such potential suicides. When the ghost gets a firm grip in the victim's emotions, there may be no turning back, no escape, no faking. So the volunteer may not survive.

But survive or not, this volunteer will perform an exemplary community service–that of laying a homicidal ghost to rest, and reducing the area's mortality rate.

They are still looking for a volunteer.

INDIAN JOE

Nobody knows how long ago it started and nobody cares, really, but ever since then the murderous ghost of Indian Joe has been loose in the Uwharries. You're apt to see him at the scene of any violent death.

That's the way this ghost perpetuates himself, by soaking up all the raw and morbid emotion and energy surrounding such deaths: the moaning and groaning and frenzied pleading for help from the dying and injured, the weeping and lamentations from friends and lovers, the stunned amazement of the investigators of such tragedies, the sudden leftover "dying wish" mentality of the victims left hanging in the air.

All these decadent and negative expressions energize the ghost and sustain him on the prowl for the next violent death.

Normal deaths, quick and easy or lingering and troubled, never excite him. It takes a lot of blood and gore, with some mystery and intrigue thrown in, to activate this ghost.

Even so, he's a bit finicky and selective about which violent deaths to monitor.

For instance, traffic deaths are so common that they rarely attract him anymore. He used to love public lynchings and firing squad executions, but these don't happen much either. He loves drownings and poisonings, fire victims, and industrial accident victims. Wars and war casualties would keep him happy, but there aren't many wars in the Uwharries, and he seldom ventures out of the area. If it's a long time between homicides, he may choose to materialize around a traffic fatality, especially a multiple death accident.

One of the plainest reports of this ghost's sightings occurred in such a mishap many decades ago when a car occupied by two drunks slammed into the big rock on the Bad Curve-Big Rock Road, killing both men.

Midge Galloway saw it and told about it.

"They passed me, wide open, a ways back and I knew they were going to crash, so I followed. I heard 'em hit Big Rock—sounded like dynamite going off. When I got in sight, a fire had started from the spilled gasoline and it kept getting bigger. Half, two-thirds of that car looked like it was smashed flat into that rock, almost like Big Rock itself was shoved back, and Big Rock is big as a house. I heard both men shrieking and pleading before they died.

"That's when I saw the ghost of ol' Indian Joe. I saw 'im plain because the moon was up and it was almost full. He leaned out from behind that rock up near the top. Kinda misty, smoky like, bigger than life. Once he appeared, he didn't move much. Just like he was part of that rock. I couldn't see his face much. But I did see that headband with the feather sticking out. No tomahawk. Just the feather like other folks have described. I know it was Indian Joe!

"He stayed right there till some of the family members came to the scene. You never heard such crying and taking on. It looked like ol' Joe leaned forward just a little and maybe got a little lower so he'd be closer. Don't think anybody else saw 'im. They were too busy looking at the carcasses of pore ol' Pumkin' Talbolt and Big Boy Bowman. Both of 'em killed by the impact, then burned to death, too. I stayed there till the sheriff and the undertaker loaded the remains into bags and put 'em in the ambulance. Then I looked around and ol' Indian Joe was gone."

Other vague hand-me-down reports indicate that the ghost of Indian Joe has been spotted at the scene of violent deaths of all descriptions—murders by firearms, axes, stabbing, clubbing, hanging, drowning, falling, burning, suffocating, mutilation, starvation, as well as suicides and accidental deaths of many varieties.

In some cases observers glimpse him momentarily. Other times people see him repeatedly. Always the image is life-size or larger, and misty or smoky, but unmistakable.

Three trademarks identify the ghost. He wears a headband with a feather over his long floppy hair. Or an armband around his upper arm. Or he wields a tomahawk in his upraised hand, ready to strike.

Some folks say Indian Joe dates back to pre-Revolutionary War days when Indians still roamed the Uwharries and were reluctant to give up this paradisiacal land to the white homesteaders. Indians resented getting pushed out of their homeland, and clashes with white settlers occurred.

Indian Joe became a renegade loner, unaffiliated with any family, community, or tribe of his kinsmen. He stole from the settlers, carrying off cured meat, butchering livestock, raiding food storage places, taking weapons and ammunition.

If people got in his way, he killed them. Sometimes he went out of his way to kill them, even slaughtering whole families.

The settlers tried to retaliate. Law enforcement was ineffective. Posses tried to run Indian Joe down, with little luck. Once at dusk they saw him leaving a home with loot on his horse. They fired at him as he entered the woods. When they reached the spot they found a trail of blood. Darkness ended the hunt. They camped, planning to resume the trail at daylight, but morning brought two inches of snow, obliterating the bloodspot trail.

More killings and larceny followed, all attributed to Indian Joe. He picked isolated cabins and homesteads. Sometimes days passed before his gory misdeeds became known. A few times he set fire to the homes to cover his crime. Neighbors had to sift through the rubble to find remains and account for the occupants. Most often when he killed he used his bow and arrow, or his tomahawk or knife, weapons that did not create a lot of noise.

The men of the area made renewed efforts to find and exterminate Indian Joe, but he stayed on the go. Seldom did his pursuers find his campfire or any lodging place. Speculation was that he traveled by night and mostly hid out during the day. They tried to set traps for him. They set up an ambush along a trail they knew he traveled. They left a woman and small children outside an isolated homestead all day, while two armed men stood guard inside at the door and window, ready to blast Indian Joe if he came within range.

But no one could outsmart Indian Joe. Even the most expert woodsman was no match for his cunning in the wilderness.

Then one afternoon they spotted him.

On their way home after a long search, half-a-dozen horsemen, armed to the teeth, decided to check by the Levine Burroughs homestead. The posse topped a rise and stopped in astonishment. Heavy smoke rose over the Burroughs home. Indian Joe, on horseback, raced toward the woods.

"Shoot him, shoot him!" the leader ordered.

Muskets boomed. Indian Joe's horse stumbled and appeared to fall as it vanished into the woods, probably hit and severely wounded by one of the musket balls.

"Mullen, you hurry down to the Burroughs home and see if you can pull anybody out of that fire," the leader ordered. "The rest of us will chase him down. His horse is shot out from under him. He may be hurt or crippled, too. He's headed toward the river. Come on, let's go! We've got to catch him and kill that bastard before he gets there."

Five horsemen galloped to the woods. A wounded horse lay on the ground, whinnying pitifully. Its broken legs twisted awkwardly. Blood poured out of a stomach hole. One man fired a shot into its head.

"Fan out. Keep your guns ready. Let's flush him out of here," the leader ordered.

They pushed through the trees and undergrowth, finally emerging in a clearing.

"There he goes!" a man shouted, "into the other woods. He's hurt. He's limping. He's bleeding, too!"

The leader said, "Looks like we've got him this time. These woods go up to the top of the ridge. Down the other side is the river. If he gets to the river, we'll never get him. Jackson, you go around the low end of the ridge. Get close as you can to the river. Head upstream. Maybe you can spot him if he gets there before we do. The rest of us will go after him through these woods. If he's dropping blood, that'll help."

Jackson galloped off. The others rode fast as possible into the thick woods, then abandoned their horses and scrambled upward, following a trail of disturbed leaves, broken twigs, and an occasional blood spot. At the top center of the ridge, it appeared that a person or heavy object had rolled down the other side for the trail was easy to follow.

When they got to the bottom of the ridge, Jackson met them, shaking his head and pointing with his musket barrel.

Blood spots led straight to the water's edge.

"He must have gotten here just a minute or two before I did," Jackson speculated.

"Damn!" the leader spat. "The river's got him."

They searched the river for half a mile downstream before giving up.

The river that day was swift and cold, choppy and menacing, flooding over its bank in places, and hungry for a victim.

Indian Joe was never seen again. His killings and depredations stopped. People figured he drowned in the river and the catfish ate his carcass. No one ever calculated how many people he had killed, but the number had to be substantial. His savagery became legend, embellished through the generations by hand-me-downs and folklore.

Today people in the Uwharries still refer to Indian Joe—and his ghost.

During World War II a drunken tenant farmer shot and killed his wife and son, and then turned the gun on himself. All the bodies lay amid the weeds of the backyard. Other family members cried and lamented. Neighbors gathered. Officials investigated and the undertakers finally removed the bodies about midnight.

One man reported seeing the ghost, Indian Joe.

"I saw him clearly hovering there in the nearby trees," he said. "Nobody else did, I reckon. Just sorta his waist up. There was a little breeze and when the leaves and branches moved, he moved with them. The leaves kinda rustled and whispered and this noise sounded like it coulda been coming from him. Long, bushy hair. Yep! I saw that headband with the feather in it. It was him all right."

Some claim to have spotted the ghost at the scene of drownings in rivers and lakes throughout the Uwharries. One such report focuses on Falls Lake behind Narrows Dam on the Yadkin River, before it becomes the Pee Dee at Morrow Mountain State Park.

"I saw the ghost of ol' Injun Joe," the camper said. "It had to be him. He wuz big–BIG! A misty vapor rose from the water and created a sorta screen–like fog all up and over the dam. An image appeared in it. Big, too, big as the side of a barn. It wuz the head of an Indian chief. Big headdress. Lots of feathers. Feathers hanging down on each side in front. No headband. No armband. But I did see a tomahawk raised ready to strike in front of him. There wuz some sort of faint illumination framing him because I could see his hawk-like nose, his high cheek-bones, bushy brows and his mouth. He weren't smiling. Kinda scowly and mean like."

From the top center of the high dam, this image occasionally angled down, growing smaller as it descended, to a point right over the water–presumably right over the submerged body. After a few minutes the image angled back up to the top of the dam, resuming its original size and position.

"I watched it do this a couple of times, then I got so scared, I jumped back in the tent and rolled up in my sleeping bag and stayed there, shivering, till daylight," the camper said.

Homicides and other violent deaths are the ghost's standby. This is where you are most likely to see him. Since the Uwharries go into half-a-dozen counties, this area produces enough such deaths to keep the ghost motivated.

But what if there is a lull or slowdown in such deaths and the ghost gets desperate and hungry for more morbidity input? What if he can't find enough homicidal action to sustain himself?

Speculation takes over.

The ghost of Indian Joe is strong enough to *cause* such deaths. Easily he could cause a traffic fatality. Easily he could cause homicides among street people, drifters, feuding neighbors, political rivals, romantic trian-gles, in domestic abuse, business relationships, inheritance participants, and racial situations.

What can local society do to stave off such massive deaths caused by a malevolent ghost?

Eliminate the ghost.

How do you eliminate a ghost?

Perhaps a posse of modern day ghost hunters will have better luck tracking down and eradicating the spirit of Indian Joe than did their counterparts, who tried to eliminate the real-life Indian Joe well over two hundred years ago.

THE DOORMAKER

In his younger years, Orlander Peeves needed no help to turn out his custom-made doors, which he sold to the public throughout the Uwharries. Arthritic and unable to work in his latter years, he did need some help. And he got it.

Ghosts helped him produce doors.

Folks say these same ghosts are still around to help you *if* you are as good and deserving as Orlander Peeves.

Few of us can meet that criteria, however.

Many a plea has been made to Orlander's ghosts. Some really agonizing pleas from deserving people. Repeatedly, too. But response has been minimal. The pleaders just don't measure up.

But the few folks who still know about Orlander Peeves keep on trying.

A bachelor approaching middle age, Orlander sprouted gray hair around the temples and the edge of his receding hairline. Bushy eyebrows guarded big friendly eyes, which seemed to caress you with warmth. His jowled face always smiled and greeted you with a pleasant expression and the expectancy that you and he would remain close pals forever. His long arms ended in huge hands that always knew exactly what to to.

Orlander lived in a crude cabin way out in the woods, accessible by a rough wagon road. His woodworking shop, weatherblackened and guarded by tall pines, leaned and looked like it could be blown over by a strong wind. Inside he built doors with simple machinery and hand tools. He hauled rough hewn lumber from the sawmill and converted it herein into beautiful doors of all descriptions, most of them especially customized for his customers.

He loved to produce doors. Anytime anyone needed a door, they turned to Orlander and he made it for them. Some he already had in stock. Doors for almost every application, for inside and outside, pantries, bathrooms, cupboards, cabinets, basements, scuttle holes, doors for businesses, schools, churches, palaces. Give him the measurements and Orlander produced a door to your complete satisfaction. All his doors were identifiable by their superb craftsmanship, by their obvious solidarity and durability, and by a patina of love and rustic beauty unmatched by any competitor.

Each door had a surface personality, as if it offered a message, almost as if it could and would communicate with you if you insisted. The extended personality of its builder, folks said.

Orlander began naming his doors, putting a sort of trademark and blessing on them. While all his doors were dedicated to peace, happiness, and prosperity, he put a special blessing on many. On some he engraved a symbol—a rose, a lily, a dove, a cross, praying hands, a Bible, a goblet, a halo.

He dedicated his doors to everything: peace, happiness, prosperity, fellowship, hope, faith, good health, harmony, opportunity, security, longevity, freedom, utterance, good harvests, spiritual enrichment, and common sense. When he delivered a new door to newlyweds in their first home or to an elderly couple nearing the end of their days, Orlander had a special blessing and a short but inspirational lecture.

"This is a special door made just for you," he told them in a mellow voice. "It will brighten your future. It will bring you good luck and joy and peace like you've never experienced before. You love this door and it loves you. You treat it like a friend and it'll be a friend to you. Should you have any trouble, you tell your troubles to the door."

He built specialty doors: a door to your heart, to your head, your mind, body, artistic ability, skills, future, and a door to your soul's deepest desire.

For kids he built miniature doors in frames, which would open and creak shut. He told the kids these were doors to laughter, to magic, to fairylands, to faraway places, to adventuresome places you could dream about. He urged their parents to follow through.

Along with his door ministry, Orlander was always helping people. Especially widows, orphans, the misfits, the bereaved, the sick and infirm. He helped plow their gardens, harvest crops, repair roofs and chimneys, clean out wells and springs, cut firewood and stove wood, even rebuild a burned-out family's cabin. Always he was helping people. Never could he turn down a person in need or a desperate plea for help.

The old country preacher took a special liking to Orlander, even using him as a model citizen and preaching sermons about him.

"God created many good people," he used to say from the pulpit. "But when he created Orlander Peeves, He almost outdid Himself. He did more than a day's work when He created Orlander. That man's always helping people. Always. Every day he helps someone. That's what this Bible tells us to do, help your fellow man in need, and that's what Orlander does. He's a splendid example of what this good book talks about. He don't ever ask anyone to help him. No! But he helps others all the time. And he don't ever brag about it, either. I wish this ol' world had lots more Orlanders in it."

The preacher was about the only one to visit long inside Orlander's shop. Orlander seemed to know when most visitors were coming, so he met them at the entrance. In the latter years, the shop doubled as a sanctuary—but just for two people. He and the preacher spent a lot of time talking inside. People believed the preacher even worked some with his hands helping Orlander with his doors.

Came the day when Orlander had to slow down. Gout swelled his feet and made it painful for him to stand. Rheumatism racked his joints and slow-motioned his movements. Door production slowed drastically. People began to pity poor ol' stove-up Orlander. He had to hobble with a cane to and from his workshop.

Then the door production picked up again. Within a few weeks it was back to normal levels. But who was doing the work? Not Orlander. He could hardly walk from cabin to shop. Not the preacher. Old and feeble now, he seldom came to the shop anymore. Never had Orlander hired any employees. There were no volunteers. Customers who came to the shop to pick up doors reported less noise coming from inside.

Strangely though, passersby who came close enough at night could see light from the shop's window. A sort of eerie, greenish light. But no one went to investigate.

By now commercial doors were becoming popular, and most new homebuilders opted to let the contractor provide them. So Orlander's business settled down to replacement and specialty doors.

But in his severely handicapped condition, how did he produce even those?

Nobody knew.

A few of the older people stopped by to see if they could help Orlander in his elderly infirmities, but no, he wanted no help. He had taken care of himself all his long life, so he could continue through the final stages.

Anyway, during his last year or so, Orlander apparently had regular assistance from sources unknown to most people.

Mitzen Chambly, a contemporary, studied about it a lot:

"I don't know anything for sure. I never saw any of them. Nobody else did. I'm just speculating. Everybody knows Orlander couldn't do all that work by himself. He could hardly walk. Could hardly feed himself. His mind went a little bad during that last year, too. But doors kept coming outta that shop. Pretty, new doors, good as any he ever made when he was able-bodied. He sold a few, gave away some. But we don't rightly know what happened to most of those doors he had help a-making.

"Good fairies, somebody said. Somebody else wondered if it was a case like the famous story of the old shoemaker and the elves who came at night to do his work for him. Somebody else says ghosts helped him. I think that's getting closer. Remember all those people Orlander helped? Dozens, scores, probably hundreds. Most of them dead and gone before Orlander became disabled. All good people. I think some of them came back from the grave to help Orlander in his time of need. Very much unsolicited. He would never have called them to help. They volunteered. Call them ghosts if you want to."

And all those extra doors that the ghosts turned out, doors that could not be accounted for otherwise.

Did they turn into ghost doors?

Incredible!

But incredibly strange reports and occurrences characterize the Uwharries.

Folks say it's possible to see at night in a lonely part of the Uwharries a ghostly parade of illuminated doors gyrating through the blackness, sort of like glamorous models flaunting their assets along a footlighted gangway.

And it's just possible, too, they say, if you are one of the best people anywhere in your extended community and have a pressing need for a new door in your home–you could wake up one fine morning to discover a beautiful new door already installed and in use in your home. It could be the door to your soul's deepest desire.

A few needy people still make pleas for help to the ghosts who assisted Orlander. But they might as well stop. For any reasonable expectation of positive results, the pleader must be at least half as good a person as was Orlander Peeves.

Anyway, those ghosts who came back to help Orlander, they might not have been ghosts at all.

Maybe they were angels.

THE INQUISITIVE GHOST

The hand that alights on your body–and it can light *anywhere* on your body–is gentle and tentative at first. Then it becomes more active and aggressive. Inquisitive, too, if an exploring hand can be inquisitive, and this one can. It takes its time, as if enjoying this familiar intimacy, but eventually it slowly wiggles its way along your arms to your hands and pauses there a while. This is its goal–your hands.

You are experiencing the invisible ghost hand of the Uwharries, which will continue its enigmatic exploration of the human anatomy eternally.

Unless it finds what it's looking for.

Then–who knows?

This invisible ghostly hand began its mission a long, long time ago.

When the Usher family settled in the Uwharries they didn't farm much, as did the other white settlers. Word soon got out that they were thieves, maybe killers. If a local man stopped at their home for a drink of water, they right quickly made him feel unwelcome. Rarely did they neighbor with the other settlers. They kept to themselves, the older man and woman, their two sons, and a daughter.

The public wagon road went by the Usher place close enough that passersby could see activity there.

A stranger on horseback showed up at the Usher place. But only for a day or two. After that he wasn't seen anymore. However, local passersby believed there was an extra horse in the Usher corral. Speculation in the community indicated the Ushers had murdered the man and buried his body by night.

Months later another stranger showed up and stopped at several homesteads, inquiring about his missing brother, who had come this way, carrying several hundred dollars. The description he gave fitted that of the stranger who disappeared at the Usher place. When this brother got to the Usher place, he too disappeared and was never seen again.

"The Ushers killed and robbed 'em–I know they did," old man Moses Fernwood reportedly said. "They didn't have nothing when they came here. Didn't even buy that land, just settled on it. Thieving and killing—that's all they good fer."

On holidays, especially in the summer, the settlers gathered for fun and festivity at the spring beside a big bottom field along the river. There was horse racing, picnicking, horseshoe pitching, music and some square dancing. Of course, some moonshine drinking, gambling, and skirt chasing took place, too.

Once old man Usher and his two sons came to one of these events. They kept to themselves and didn't mingle much.

One of the local farmers spotted the Ushers and approached them. This man had several hogs stolen from his pen, and he suspected the Ushers were guilty. Drunk and arrogant, he weaved up to the Ushers, accused them of stealing his hogs, and called them a thieving bunch of cutthroats.

The older Usher boy flashed a long-bladed knife and started slashing at the accuser. He cut across the neck and shoulder, then ripped him across the stomach. He would have ripped more, but some men grabbed him, pinned his arms, and took away his knife. More men kept the other Ushers at bay.

The grievously wounded man slumped to his knees, then fell on his side, a portion of his guts spilling out the hole in his stomach and onto the dirt.

Someone ran to the spring and returned with a pot of water, with which they washed his guts clean. They soaked a cloth in whiskey and swabbed out the wound. They poured whiskey into the man to kill his pain, while a horseman raced to the nearest house and returned with a big needle and stout thread. A volunteer sewed up the long gash. None of his guts were punctured.

The old folks say the man recovered and lived a long time after that.

While all the attention was on the wounded man, the Usher boy who did the knifing slipped away, a long way away, for he was never again seen in the Uwharries.

But the old man Usher, his wife, daughter, and the other son stayed on.

Horse stealing became a problem in the area. Nobody could catch the thief. Thoroughbreds, prized horses, were the targets. Such mounts brought a premium on the market. Sharp eyes monitored the Usher place. Reports were that every time horses were stolen, old man Usher or his son would disappear and stay gone for a week or two. All the neighbors believed the Ushers stole the horses, took them far away, and sold them for a fancy price. Yet there was no evidence, no proof.

What to do about the troublesome Ushers?

There was talk about setting fire to their cabin at night, and then shooting them one by one as they ran out to escape the fire. The corpses could be drug back into the fire and no one would ever know they had been shot and killed before they burned. But not enough volunteers offered to carry out such a plan. Finally a man named Morgan came up with a plan that worked. And he did it all by himself.

One of the more progressive settlers, Morgan owned a fine bunch of horses, which he kept penned inside his barn at night, especially in the wintertime. He let it be known throughout the settlement that he and his wife planned to visit relatives in eastern North Carolina, and would be gone for several weeks. He was leaving his Negro houseboy to look after the livestock.

After traveling to closer relatives only fifteen miles away, Morgan left his wife with them. He slipped back home at night and concealed himself in the barn, even sleeping right over the door opening into the penned horses. The houseboy brought his meals to the barn.

In order to open the barn door from the outside, a man had to stretch his arm and hand through a slot to work the latch. Up over this latch, Morgan positioned a razor-sharp broadaxe with a long handle, one that he could grab and use in a second. He knew, because he practiced with it during the day.

About the third night, Morgan heard a prowler outside the barn. He seized the broadaxe and waited. His eyes were accustomed to the darkness inside the barn. Reflected moonlight gave a little illumination. A horse snorted. All horse ears pointed his direction. Then a hand slid through the slot and began to work the latch. Morgan chopped downward with the broadaxe in a powerful swing. A horrible scream split the night. Footsteps scurried, then a horse galloped away, leaving behind a trail of blood.

Morgan lit a candle. On the floor under the latch lay a bloody human hand.

At daylight Morgan rounded up a few neighbors. On horseback they followed the trail of blood straight to the Usher place. But the Ushers were not there. Morgan saw fresh blood spots inside on the floor. Fire coals still glowed in the fireplace. The wagon and team were gone, as were most of the household goods. Later a man reported seeing a loaded wagon headed west, occupied by an older man and woman, and a younger woman. A younger man on horseback accompanied the wagon.

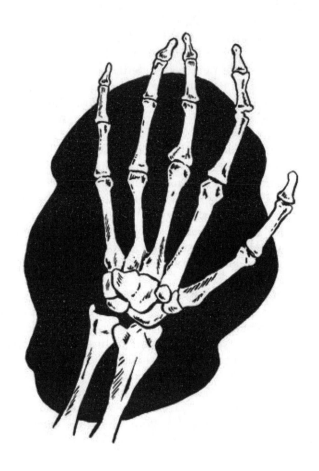

The man also reported that the younger man had a bloody rag around his stubby arm, ending about where a hand ought to be.

Morgan nailed the human hand over the barn door where it remained for many years. Buzzards, birds, animals, and insects would never touch it. The flesh rotted off, leaving bones burnished by the elements. Moonlight gave the bones an extra gleam. People journeyed for miles to stare at this human hand, and then at its remains.

An old storyteller remembers it this way:

"You know what that hand did? It had to be the hand, for the Ushers were gone. Horse stealing stopped. 'Twas never another horse stole in these parts that we heard about. The hand did it. People looked at that hand. They talked about it for years and years. A plain lesson. Plain justice. It was easy to see what horse stealing could lead to. And it cut down on other thieving, too. I know it did."

There is no record of the Ushers ever trying to retaliate for the chopped-off hand. Nobody knows what happened to them.

But the hand is still around. That is, a reminder of the hand—the ghost of the hand.

That hand became an object of intense curiosity and scrutiny. It became famous. It attained celebrity status far beyond the community. Never a day went by, hardly a night, but what passersby stopped, stood around staring at the gruesome sight, and asked about the story behind it. And Morgan always obliged.

The ghost hand became active about the time the last of the fragile hand bones deteriorated into nothingness. There was nothing left to see anymore except a few rusty nails sticking out of the decaying barn wall. As long as the barn stood, locals would bring visitors to stare at the nails and shiver through an exaggerated version of how a horse thief lost his hand. Kids would gasp, even squall, and their eyes bulged at the graphic part about the severed hand falling to the floor and its fingers moving as if trying to grasp something as the blood spurted out.

"He done wrong—and they cut off his hand," the storyteller said.

The kids recoiled into their parents' arms with this awful message framed in their minds: if I do wrong, that might happen to me!

"For a long time after that, discipline was no problem around here," the storyteller concluded.

Mert Massingale first felt the ghost hand on her body during Sunday morning services at Rollin' River Reformed Church. "I felt it sorta poke me when I got outta my buggy and tied my horse," she said. "Then, inside, I was right in the middle of the congregation when I felt it sliding around my body. That's pretty upsetting. I looked around, but nobody behind me or close by was doing anything. The hand got on my arm and went down to my hand and stayed there a little bit. And that was all. I didn't feel it anymore."

At square dances fistfights broke out when young ladies reported they were being molested by a straying hand.

Always the shocked victim recoiled and looked about to see if any real live person manipulated the hand.

No amount of jerking, shaking, or brushing off can stop the hand once it starts its exploration.

Sleepers are awakened by a mysterious hand rubbing across their bodies.

In the early days, the ghost hand preferred people who owned, rode, or worked with horses. Nowadays any individual anywhere is a potential victim.

One young driver of a vehicle with the emblem of a mustang on the side said that the hand bothered a passenger.

What the hand wants is a permanent home—a compatible person with an arm and hand it can merge with. But it has to be a precise merger, an arm and hand that perfectly fits and suits the ghost hand to a T.

That's why the ghost hand keeps on looking. And it apparently enjoys the looking.

So when you feel that invisible ghost hand on your body, checking you out and measuring your hand for that precise fit, you could be its choice for merger.

What happens when this ghost hand merges with the hand of its real life soul mate?

Likely the new mergee will be influenced to begin nefarious activities similar to those which produced the ghost hand in the first place—activities which might lead to a newly severed human hand displayed in a public place.

KEG OF MYSTERY

Stomp Feddlesom saw it first. Then Phelps Turner. Then Tulo Bitts. Apparently then a bunch of people saw it.

All told essentially the same story.

"Scared the daylights outta me. Of course, it was nighttime. Pretty moon a-shinin'. Real light night. I could see good out there on Dusty Owl Road. There about where the gully washes over the road in a heavy rain. Kinda lonesome up there, you know. It come sorta crashin' and clunkin' down the bank on my left, a few yards in front of me, then bumped across the road and down through the brush below the road on my right. Passed right across in front of me. Nothin' in front of it, nothin' behind it that I could see. Everythin' quiet and peaceful before it appeared, the same way after it vanished. Scared me so bad. I run home like the devil was after me and flopped inside and couldn't talk for ten minutes."

What did he see?

"The keg. The whiskey keg. That ten-gallon keg of moonshine whiskey rollin' across the road. The same one other people have seen and told about. I was walkin', but if I had been ridin' my mule, ol' Kate woulda spooked and throwed me off and run away back home like other wagon and buggy horses have done. The keg just sorta bumped along, not too fast, 'bout like a man walkin'. It was kinda faded. Brownish gray. Beat up a little and scarred after bouncin' over all them rocks and roots for years. Still full of moonshine and heavy. I know. I could hear it a-sloshin' and a-crunchin' the gravel. If that keg would sneak up and hit yuh, it could knock you down and break a leg. Maybe bounce up and down on top of you and kill you.

"And just think. A charred keg full of aged moonshine. First-grade moonshine, too. That's the only kind ol' man Bascom would turn out and put in a charred keg. Oh, he'd sell you second and third run stuff, but he'd tell you it was bad and he'd never put that bad stuff in a keg. This moonshine here in this keg is first-run, high quality, high proof, copper pot booze as good as any homemade stuff you'll ever find anywhere. All that agin'. And agitatin'. It'll be worth a month's wages. That's the kind of booze people would even kill for."

While the ghost keg of booze originated in the hills around Tuckertown, it was reported on many roads and trails, even occasionally tumbling through a barnyard or along a pasture fence where it spooked all the livestock. Folks claimed it had been seen around Uwharrie, Eldorado, Ophir, Eleaser, Abner, Black Ankle, even over in the Birkheads. Any unidentified nocturnal noise could be attributed to the ghost keg running into something and causing the dogs to bark and the guineas to potrack and the goosebumps to ripple over your skin.

Most everybody knew ol' man Bascom and his two rangy sons dominated the moonshine business in the Tuckertown territory. The law knew it, too, but affable Sheriff Tinney never bothered a moonshiner unless the complaints got too heavy. Then he usually sent word ahead of the raiding party, so nobody got arrested. Heck, most of the the men had seen Sheriff Tinney take a swig of Bascom's moonshine, anyway. If you wanted good moonshine, Bascom's was the way to go.

Bascom moonshined from May till October, then hid his copper still and equipment till the following spring. Much of his first-run product sold immediately from the still. The rest he stored in charred wooden kegs of ten, twenty, and thirty-gallon capacity. These he buried in the ground at secret locations, and replenished them as needed from subsequent distilling operations. When a customer wanted a quart or half-gallon fruit jar filled, Bascom or a son went alone to the secret depository and used a simple hand pump to extract the desired amount. No one except the owner and one or two trusted helpers knew about these secret caches and where they kept the hand pump hidden.

Buzz Riddle wanted more than a quart. More than a half gallon, or full gallon. He wanted enough to keep him drunk for weeks. He wanted a whole keg full.

Buzz was the community's notorious alcoholic. All he wanted was to stay drunk, or at least half drunk, all the time. At the half drunk stage he worked a little at the sawmill, at new ground clearings, at harvest time. His earnings went to Bascom for booze. When his booze and money ran out, he pleaded to buy booze on credit. For years Buzz pestered Bascom to sell him a whole keg, which would keep him soused for weeks. But always on credit. This Bascom would never do. All his moonshine transactions were strictly cash with trusted customers, a category not applicable to Buzz Riddle.

But Buzz persisted. He became a nuisance. He pestered Bascom to no end. He'd show up at the Bascom home, stagger around and wave his arms and demand a keg of moonshine. He'd rave and rant. Sometimes he dropped to his knees and begged. Sometimes he threatened to tell the sheriff. Once he stole a pig and tried to trade it to Bascom for booze. Sometimes he got so angry and mean that the Bascom boys had to escort him off their property. Always he swore he'd be back.

After a dry spell of a few days, his alcohol-busted mind led him to take drastic action.

On an early December Saturday night, Buzz borrowed his family's mule and wagon and drove to a secluded spot on the backside of the Bascom property. He walked through the forest carrying a long-handled shovel. He stopped in a patch of woods near the Bascom residence. He knew about where the Bascoms kept their moonshine buried in kegs. Buzz concealed himself in the bushes and waited. Moon and starlight sifted through the trees for adequate vision.

More moonshine customers came on Saturday nights. To fill the orders, the Bascoms used a flashlight or lantern on the path to the woods. Only one came at a time. He knelt low over the spot, raked back the leaves and litter, then used the hand pump to fill the container, usually a fruit jar, from the subterranean keg. The Bascom boys came and got the booze for the first several customers. Buzz waited. He didn't want the boys. He wanted the old man. Bascom was strict about the Sabbath; he sold no moonshine on Sunday. Midnight marked the beginning of Sunday, and Bascom always served the last customer at midnight. The rest of the family went to bed and let him secure everything.

A few minutes before midnight, Buzz saw a light coming down the path into the woods. He knew it was Bascom by his size and the way he walked. The old man got down on his knees at a new location, raked away the litter, and started to pump moonshine into his container. Buzz came up behind, swung the metal end of the shovel in a terrific arc, and bashed the old man in the back of the head. He slumped over, kicked a bit, and died on the leaves. Using the shovel, Buzz excavated the keg of moonshine, replaced it with Bascom's body, covered it with all the excavated material, then smoothed over the top with leaves and forest floor litter just like the surrounding area.

He rolled and lugged the keg of moonshine back to the wagon, took it home, hid it in a safe place, and used its contents to stay drunk for weeks.

Meantime, it took the Bascom boys all day Sunday to find their father's body. They knew immediately who had killed him and why. But Sheriff Tinney couldn't find enough evidence to make a case, so he didn't arrest anyone. The Bascoms didn't push it. They bided their time. They knew how to get their man and avenge their father's death.

Weeks passed. Then a month or two.

Buzz finally sobered up and began meandering about the community. He looked for a job to earn enough money to buy booze. But no job. No booze. He became desperate for drink. He even went by the Bascom place and pleaded for booze on credit. The Bascom boys ran him off.

As he left the Bascom premises Buzz's demented mind produced a memory that led to an idea. That patch of woods back there–a shovel–the heavy keg with its contents sloshing–

That night the Bascom boys, each with a loaded rifle, concealed themselves in the bushes amid the trees near where their father had died. They almost knew they would have a visitor.

Sure enough, along about bedtime, a rustling in the leaves alerted them. A figure approached unsteadily through the moonlight. They could tell it was Buzz Riddle. Buzz kicked around in the leaves and rubble looking for the soft cover over a keg of moonshine. He found a spot, dropped to his knees, and quickly raked out all the loose material, then used his shovel to excavate the keg. He wrestled the keg to the surface. He squatted and lifted the keg almost waist high.

Two shots rang out, almost together. The rifle slugs struck Buzz squarely in the chest. He staggered backward, the heavy keg slipping from his hands. It slid down his legs and bounced on the ground, the momentum taking it on into the bushes.

The Bascom boys stuffed Buzz's body into the hole, refilled it with all the excavated material, then smoothed over the top with forest floor litter comparable to the surrounding area. The site looked as if it had never been disturbed.

They kept the shovel, convinced it was the same tool that had killed their father.

They looked for the keg of moonshine, but could not find it.

Not many tears fell over Buzz Riddle's disappearance. People said he probably died drunk in the woods somewhere and the buzzards ate his carcass. Or he fell in the river and drowned and the catfish ate him. Sheriff Tinney poked around a little, asked a few questions, and considered his work done when he labeled the case a mysterious disappearance.

What about that keg of moonshine that fell out of the dying man's hands and rolled into the bushes?

Uwharrie folks say it never stopped rolling. That it's still rolling today. That it will keep on rolling into eternity.

In fact, there are two ghosts you may encounter in this area as you travel slowly on moonlit nights along the back roads and lanes in these ancient hills.

One is the ghost of a man whose countenance is contorted in a plea for help. His hands are stretched toward you imploringly. Some say his fingers are curled as if ready to grip the edges of something heavy. The handle of a shovel may be visible under his arm.

The other is the ten-gallon keg of moonshine that rolls across the road in front of you. While it may be tempting, don't try to stop it or catch it or follow it. It's heavy enough to knock you down and break a leg, maybe even pound up and down on top of you.

On the other hand, everyone agrees that the keg contains a potent substance of potential benefit to a lot of people. Addicts and alcoholics want to capture the keg and gulp its contents recklessly. The keg will not submit to such negative use. However the keg might cooperate if people of higher caliber will use its contents responsibly. Individuals in the latter category will have to approach the keg to find out. If such a union is successful, the Uwharrie keg could alert all its counterparts throughout the South to do likewise, and there would be a massive uprising of kegs of quality moonshine from scores of forgotten burial sites. Logically the kegs would prefer such positive utilization before deterioration causes the booze to leak into the ground and be lost forever.

So until the right person comes along to proposition it, the Uwharrie keg will keep on rolling. Displaced and dispossessed, it is looking for a home or for proper utilization, whichever comes first.

It can't go back to its original home because a body is stuffed in there.

THE DRY MAN

For most farmers in the Uwharries, Saturday was a slacker work day than the preceding five. Work hard for five days, then catch up on the odds and ends and miscellaneous on Saturdays, like maintenance chores, going to the grist mill, helping your neighbor with some special project, cleaning up the church and grounds for Big Meeting, road work, visiting with friends, maybe even a wagon trip with the family to the general store or to the nearest town or village, considered a special treat.

That's why Friday nights were added to Saturday nights for square dances and partying for young folks all up and down Rollin' River.

Oldsters accepted it only gradually and grudgingly.

Saturday night shindigging was practiced everywhere. Everyone knew Sunday was a holy day with no farm work allowed. So if you didn't get home until the wee hours, you could sleep late on Sunday morning, although church-going families made you get up in time to go to the service, regardless. Those who partied on Friday nights and got home in the wee hours finally convinced their elders to let them sleep late the next morning because the Saturday work schedule was less demanding.

Another reason for adding Friday nights to the weekend entertainment was Beauregard Burns. Everyone called him "Bo." Bo was a fiddler. And what a fiddler! He made the fiddle sing and cry, plead and caress and croon lullabies to you. Within earshot, you were captivated by that fiddle and pulled into any gathering. Fast or slow, swingy or waltzy, Bo could fiddle all day and night. Two days in a row. He wore out teams of other musicians who accompanied him on the guitar, mandolin, and banjo. Listeners eventually became exhausted and had to leave or sleep some. But no one ever downplayed Bo's fiddling.

Bo thrived on fiddling. If many hours passed without it, he began to wilt. That's why he played at weddings, funerals, reunions, revivals, corn shuckings, commencements, and other special events. If ever the shadow of a fiddler's elbow rubbed holes in the wall, it must have been Bo's elbow, because he played constantly.

Always the Friday and Saturday night square dances were held at Puckett's Place, a large, two-story log home with a spacious front room on the Union County side of Rollin' River. Folks on the opposite side of the river had to travel for miles in either direction before they could cross at a ford or over a low-water bridge. This made it most inconvenient for the across-the-river attendees.

Finally they worked out a partial solution. Within sight of Puckett's Place, they found the remains of an Indian fish trap in the bed of the river. Roughly semi-circular in shape, it channeled the water to a central point. Many of the stepping-stone-type rocks had washed away in floodwater. Young men of the community replaced these missing rocks, added more, flattened logs, and soon had a substantial walkway across the river at normal low-water conditions. However, at least once or twice a year after heavy rainfall, ol' Rollin' River rampaged over its banks and left destruction in its wake. Torrents of muddy water slammed into banks at bends, smashing bridges, sweeping away bateaus, canoes, piers, and everything else it could reach.

The boys tired of repairing the stepping-stone walkway. They tried other ways of safely crossing the river for themselves and their dates—a small raft, bateau, canoe, horse and buggy, horseback, a crude swinging bridge, but none were satisfactory. Mostly they just walked across at the shallowest point, rolling up pants legs, hiking dresses and holding high their shoes and stockings. Sometimes the robust men picked up and carried their diminutive female partners across the river.

But no matter what method they used in crossing, invariably their shoes and clothing got wet from the river water.

All but Sculley Wand, that is.

His clothing never got wet. No one ever learned how he did it.

He could cross the river at flood times—the water high, swift, and mean—and emerge on the other side perfectly dry.

Sculley was one of half a dozen big-eyed children belonging to the Widow Wand, who lived in a cabin on the hillside up from the village. There was no husband or father present. Folks speculated that you could wave a magic wand and another offspring would appear. When Sculley reached his teenage years, he had a reputation for strangeness and unique ways of helping people.

Keeping dry and helping others to stay dry was the strangest.

When Sculley started going to the dance, he crossed the river like the others, but never did his shoes or pants legs get wet. Others noticed and began to question him about it. So he held back a little. He waited till the other crossers got out of sight. Then he just appeared on the other side. If anyone tried to watch or spy on him, he walked to a secluded part of the river where there were no witnesses. Then he just appeared on the other side and joined the others, who were trying to smooth out their wet clothing.

Then Sculley got a girlfriend, Ruth Ann, and they started going to the dances together. Both crossed the river dry and comfortable, much to the envy of the wet and disgruntled crossers.

When Rollin' River rose out of its banks, the others gave up on crossing and stayed home. But Sculley and Ruth Ann crossed safely and dryly and went on to the dance. They came back home the same way.

Rufe Allen saw them return late one night. Everyone knew Sculley and Ruth Ann had crossed the flooded river and gone to the dance, although no one else could do so. Only yards from the water's edge, he leaned against a tree, watching the torrent sweep by in the moonlight.

"There they were, just like that," he reported, snapping his fingers. "Nothing was there. Then, all of a sudden, there they were. Both of 'em. Dry as a starched shirt. It looked like he had been carrying her up in his arms, because he was letting her down on her feet when I saw them."

Some of the girls tried to talk to Ruth Ann about it, but she would tell them nothing. Just smile mysteriously.

Slowly a pattern began to emerge. For a buck a head, Sculley would set other people across the river, safely and dryly. But he did it his way. You had to do it his way or not cross.

Always he preferred to do it privately without any witnesses. But, inevitably, probing eyes watched from afar and from concealment. All reported the same story.

Sculley insisted that his passengers wear blindfolds or keep their eyes tightly closed. To be sure, he stretched a band of black fabric over their eyes and knotted it behind their head. From behind, he put his arms around the passenger and gripped tightly. A second later, they were both across the river and he was untying the blindfold. How he got back across so quickly no one figured out, but here he was back and ready for the next passenger. He was available when they were ready to come back across.

All were treated the same–big, little, male, female, boy, girl, dog. He blindfolded them and gripped them tightly from behind. Weight didn't seem to matter, although no one ever reported him trying to transport a large animal, vehicle, or heavy object across the river. Just people.

Lehigh Bell speculated about it a lot.

"Some people think he had a special gift, like Jesus, and could walk on the water and that's how he got people across," he said. "But, hell no! That's not how he done it. Much too slow. He took me across and back two or three times. You could feel his arms around you real tight. Just close your eyes for a second or two, then open them and you're on the other side and he's already back to get somebody else.

"We didn't think so much about it back then. Just a special person with a special gift like some country folks had. You know, like witching water, casting spells, talking out fire, making warts go 'way and curing all manner of sickness. Sculley could get people across the river. And man he did it!"

An old country preacher called Sculley's gift a miracle, a divine gift, and tried to get him to use it in a religious way. But Sculley didn't take to religion very well, although there was some indication that he did slow down on his passenger crossings in his later years and concentrate more on select people who had a genuine need to cross the river. Too, there were some sketchy reports that he aided in total immersion baptisms in the river. Because the aged preacher was weak and partially disabled, he persuaded Sculley to do the manual act of baptizing the subject, while the preached remained on the bank doing the verbal part. Sculley soused the subject completely under, then raised him with the water pouring off. Then the subject walked back to the bank and climbed out—he and his clothing perfectly dry.

No one knows exactly what happened to Sculley in the end, nor if he and Ruth Ann left any descendants. Advancing age apparently slowed the frequency of his eyeblink river crossings.

Many scores of years ago, the Puckett Place burned to the ground late one weekend night. No trace of it remains. Several people were lost in this fire and subsequent activity. Sculley and Ruth Ann could have been among them.

Of unknown origin, the fire occurred in the late wee hours after all the dancing and music ended. It spread quickly and devoured the old house. A few people, especially those from more distant places, often spent the remainder of the night in the log house, sleeping on couches and on blankets piled on the floor. Sculley and Ruth Ann did this occasionally. That night flaming debris fell on and injured most of these people as they scurried to escape the collapsing house. Most of them ran and jumped into the river to put out their flaming clothing and ease the pain of their burning flesh.

Sadly the river consumed them. It grabbed them like a gigantic marine monster on the prowl for anything alive. The victims had no chance of escape. Swollen and mean, the river writhed like a huge snake. It seemed to snarl and mutter moist messages of mirth and satisfaction. The bodies washed far downstream. Halfway to the ocean, some speculated. No one ever found the bodies.

Today new roads and bridges facilitate the river crossings in the Uwharries.

However, there are some vague reports that the ghost of Sculley Wand might still look for passengers up and down Rollin' River. In fact, he might look along any river or sizable creek throughout the Uwharries, any stream too wide for stepping stones or a footlog.

Laborers on a bridge construction project years ago claimed they spotted a misty image of a man at the river's edge. Then, just seconds later, there it was on the opposite side.

Hikers and hunters claim to have seen similar ghostly images along water courses; even experienced what feels like strong arms coiling around them from behind.

Urgency, a strong need to get across the river quickly, apparently helps the ghost to materialize more readily.

So if you become stranded at the river's edge with a genuine need to get across, just close your eyes tightly for a few seconds. When you open them, you might find yourself on the other side.

It might help, too, if you have a dollar in your pocket.

STREET-WALKING FLOOZY

There's a creek somewhere in the Uwharries that if you cross at a certain point, your hair, no matter how well groomed, quickly turns into an unruly mess. Especially women's hair. The longer the hair, the messier it gets. Loose ends flop and dangle. Hundreds of such loose ends crowd under each other and weave themselves into a matted mess which can take hours to undo. Curls come out. Waves unwave. Ponytails, pig tails, French twists, big buns on top, they all come out within seconds. The scent of recently permed hair is unpleasant, for it becomes unpermed here.

All this takes place instantaneously.

If you cross the right creek at the right place.

One woman said that crossing the creek way back yonder in the old days made her great-grandmother's hair turn her into a street-walking floozy.

Reparations came fast and furiously.

Whenever a well-groomed woman discovered her hair suddenly in tatters and tangles, repairs had to be made immediately. More often than not, repairs took hours. Which meant visits and social activities had to be called off. Hosts had to be notified. Apologies and explanations had to be made. Hurt feelings had to be mitigated.

Female victims of this hair vandalism were thoroughly frustrated and puzzled. They experienced it again and again without ever learning the cause. They browbeat their menfolk into watching and waiting and trying to solve these serial cases of mutilated hair. But no one ever figured it out. Marriages even broke up over it.

This hair mutilation produced many mad, mad, mad women.

It also produced a mad, mad, mad ghost.

This ghost with the specialized activity likely is still on the job at that certain crossing on that certain creek. Probably it's madder than ever now, because it doesn't get many victims anymore.

Nobody knows its location.

There are scores, probably hundreds, of forgotten creek crossings in the Uwharries. Someone called this one "Balding Creek," and the name became the one most often associated with the ghost. But where is Balding Creek? It doesn't appear on any map or in any community memoirs. Ask an oldster and he begins: "Well–" but he never gets anywhere.

However, there is an ironic appropriateness to the name when you learn the rest of the story.

*   *   *

Mavoleen Maddix grew up in a privileged environment. She had what she wanted, all she wanted, most of the time. Her parents were well-to-do people by Uwharrie standards, with farming, horse trading, and land dealing enterprises. Whatever the skill or activity, Mavoleen excelled at it. At home, church, school, community functions, Mavoleen was the model, the one to emulate.

Reaching her early teens, Mavoleen developed into a lovely young woman. Long auburn-blondish hair crowned her voluptuous figure, which she never tired of parading. Friendly and flirtatious, she charmed everyone with her sweetness and her genuine capacity to care and share.

By the time she reached her mid-teens, Mavoleen developed a passion for boys. And men. Any male who could give her what she wanted. She went to almost any extreme to get it. Her escapades shocked the community and generated exaggerated gossip–the kind of gossip so titillating that one whispers it.

Devilish younger boys tried following Mavoleen and her boyfriend, all the while fantasizing about what they might experience with Mavoleen when they grew older. They reported Mavoleen and her boyfriend cavorting in buggies, wagons, in the barnloft and outbuildings, behind the school house, on the church steps, in the graveyard, amid the orchard, under the haystacks, at the ford in the creek, and in the bushes and trees all along the roads.

Her parents had no control over her. Warnings did no good. They locked her in her room, but she invariably broke out. Teachers and the country preacher tried to counsel her, but to no avail. Her contemporaries had all but abandoned her. No mother would dare let her daughter associate with this notorious strumpet, one of the milder names used to describe her now.

Something had to be done. Mavoleen had to be restrained and punished.

The community hierarchy gathered–the preacher, deacons, school teacher, constable, the older and wiser. The parents had given up, telling the community leaders to take whatever action they thought appropriate. It took a long time. The men never did decide. Several older women said let them handle it.

Next day a bunch of women forced Mavoleen to accompany them to the ford in the creek. There they forcibly bound her hands and feet, stripped her, sat her on a rock, and held her head and body in a firm grip while the others cut off all her long hair right down to the scalp. The clipped hair fell in the water and floated downstream. Then they shaved a wide streak across the top of her head.

All the while, she spat and cursed her tormentors, alternately shrieking and pleading with them, promising to retaliate and get even.

They freed her. She ran home, sobbing hysterically, one hand trying to cover her shorn head. The punishment worked. Mavoleen stayed home, avoided visitors, and tried to keep her head covered. Boys lost interest in her. No friends came by. She dropped out of school and church. Moody and crushed, she mostly stayed in her room, sobbing and occasionally venting her frustration with loud cries of anguish.

Weeks and months passed. When her hair grew back out to an attractive length, the women descended again, taking possession of her and forcing her to submit to another haircut to the scalp. This time they shaved a large X on top of her head.

The women did this several more times. Mavoleen was no longer beautiful physically or spiritually. She became a recluse and an object of pity. Everyone shunned her. She had no friends now. Came the day when she could take it no longer.

She crept out of the house, went by the barn, and took a few objects with her. She walked unobserved through the brush and trees to a small lake in the creek near the ford. In shoulder-deep water, she fastened a heavy log chain around her waist and neck, then tied heavy plow shovels to it. She sighed and slipped under the water to the bottom.

Days passed before they found and recovered her body—what was left of it. The catfish had been feeding.

At the funeral the old preacher had few kind words to say about Mavoleen. Instead he preached in general terms about sin always getting punished, and unrepentant sinners always paying the ultimate price. He talked about never leaving the straight and narrow, and how the righteous always win in the end. They buried her in the church cemetery, practically under the same spot where she had once been accused of fornicating.

A few months passed. And then it started. The hair mutilations.

This creek crossing was a popular one in its day, and most families forded here frequently. Women going to and from church noticed it first. As they crossed the creek, their hair flew out wild and unmanageable. Buggies parked along the road near the creek. Womenfolk stood on the ground, fussing with their hair. Most elected to go straight home rather than be seen with unkempt hair.

All the women who participated in Mavoleen's punishment experienced hair mutilation at the crossing. So did other females. Men got off more lightly, only those with long hair had any trouble there.

All of the victims agreed that it was the ghost of Mavoleen Maddix fulfilling her promise to get even with all those who cut her hair and shaved her head.

Some victims reported a laugh, especially at night, a gloating, distinctively female laugh as their hair frizzled into shambles.

"It felt like and sounded like she would gladly cut off all our hair and shave our heads, too, if she could have," one victim remembered.

No matter if your hair was in curlers, if it had combs and ribbons holding it in place, if you fastened it down tightly under a scarf, bonnet, a hat or helmet—when you crossed that creek at that ford, your hair went into uncontrollable gyrations.

No matter, either, if you crossed on foot, horseback, buggy, wagon, on your mom's back, footlog or whatever, your hair went wild.

The locals tried first-time, visiting women at the crossing. The same thing happened to them.

It happened no other place. Just here.

Women demanded that the men find another crossing, which they did, a couple of miles away. Despite this detour, the new crossing became the popular way to travel. The old crossing became unused and forgotten.

Would it be possible now, today, to find this location and resurrect this ghost?

Possible, perhaps, but unlikely.

Even today, nobody wants to look like a street-walking floozy.

Slow down a little and pay attention the next time you cross a stream in the Uwharries. If you feel a tugging or messing of your hair, you might be near Mavoleen's ghost.

Then you might develop the ability to steer your rivals and your enemies this way, so Mavoleen's ghost can practice on their hair.

To be safe, the next time you're on your way to church, to a wedding, funeral, prom, party, or whatever, don't take a shortcut through the back roads.

As mad and vindictive as Mavoleen's ghost is, it probably is seeking new victims in new locations in the Uwharries. You might be next.

THE HEXED GHOST

How do you unhex a hexed ghost?

No one seems to know.

It's not as simple as unhexing a real live person.

People in the Uwharries would like to know how, for a hexed ghost has been bothering them for well over a hundred years now. No real big trouble, just mischievous, nuisance trouble. But even these mildly destructive acts grow tiresome after a while.

If there is no obvious explanation for the vandalism, most always nocturnal, then it's usually attributed to "ol' Marr".

Infrequently some unexplained benevolent act will occur in a homestead or in a community. Some people, albeit reluctantly, give ol' Maar credit for the positive act, also.

Through the generations, he has received credit for thousands of acts—a few good ones, but most of them on the negative side.

"He must have a leetle bit of a conscience," an oldster says. "And it bothers him some, for once in a while, he'll do something good. Ye 'member that time Joe Larson's prize pony busted through the gate and ran off? Ol' Maar rounded him up, put him back in and latched the gate.

"Ye 'member that fire at Boss Bradley's cornshucking? They had a lantern sittin' on a little shelf where the men were putting up the shucks. They got through and went to the house to eat. A mule lammed into the wall on the other side and knocked the lantern off into them dry shucks. A fire started. Nobody around to see it. It coulda burned up the whole barn. But it didn't. It got put out. Later, when they discovered it, they figured out what happened. The mules' watering trough at the well, all the way full, had been lifted and brought to the shuck shed and dumped on the fire and put it out. That watering trough full of water—four men couldn't a-moved it. But ol' Maar did."

Ol' Maar did some mean things, too.

Things like taking a wheel off the wagon and hiding it in the barn loft. Turning the pigs loose. Letting loose the chickens to wreck havoc in the vegetable garden. Turning over a beehive. Pushing over the outhouse. Turning the mailbox around backwards. Placing a board over the chimney top to smoke up the house. Tying knots in a cow's tail and a mule's tail. Putting burrs under the mule's collar and under the horse's saddle. Unwinding all the rope on the well windlass. Knocking over shocks of wheat in the grain field. Dulling the blade on the scythe. Blocking the driveway with a mess of rocks. Jumbling up the rails in a rail fence.

And hundreds more.

Josiah Everhart even accused ol' Maar of draining his fishpond and letting all his fish die.

Mose Bleeker planted a big field of corn one year. He said ol' Maar brought in a flock of crows, which scratched up and ate all the seed corn before it could germinate.

Hammer-toe Morris believed it was ol' Maar who pulled off his ripe pumpkins and let them roll downhill to squash against the rocks.

There just wasn't much devilment that ol' Maar couldn't do, wouldn't do, or hadn't already done.

He didn't jeopardize anyone's life. He didn't cause any major damage. He just did enough annoyance and nuisance to keep people stirred up and on edge.

They called him a vandal, a prankster, a trickster, a practical jokester. And a lot of worse names, too.

Before he became a ghost, ol' Maar was a man, a middle-aged farmer named Ransom Barley. A likable man who didn't bother anybody, Ransom loved everyone and went out of his way to help his neighbors and anyone else in need. How he antagonized the old witch woman who hexed him, nobody knows for sure. Some believe she got mad because Ransom would not give her a fine shoat pig from his pen.

But hex him she did.

Everybody knew old Tilda Sammers was witchy. Scrawny, beak-nosed, and mean-eyed, she muttered and snarled like a vicious dog, and hunched up her shoulders when anyone came near her shack. If you met her walking, likely she'd take a swing at you with her walking stick. Strange lights, noises, and scents came from her shack, especially at night.

When Ransom caused her temper to flare, she zapped him with a spell, right then and there. It may have happened by the creek where the witch went to pick berries and where Ransom drove some of his livestock for watering.

"She spelled him all right," an old man remembers. "She put a spell on Ranse like nobody else has ever experienced before or since. Folks called it a troublesome spell. It sho' was trouble, all right. An' he never did get over it. Course, he didn't live so long after that, anyway."

Troublemaker would be a better description.

Ransom's disposition changed quicker than overnight. His family said so. Everyone else did, too. From a friendly, mild, helpful individual, Ransom turned sinister and hostile. Contempt spread over his face, and his evil eyes drilled into you. He kicked at dogs and kids and spat in your face and shrilled out profane words.

Meese Pickens caught Ransom tearing up a big sign at his general store and ran him off. A farmer coming back from the mill said Ransom ran up behind his wagon and pulled off a sack of cornmeal and let it bust open on the ground. He leered at women as long as he could see them. Practically every farm and home experienced some sort of vandalism.

Then the big stuff started.

It didn't happen every night. Just two or three times a month, maybe. Some said on nights when the moon was full, Ransom changed from a man into an animal. Beast, rather. Or half beast. A few people claimed to have seen this half man, half beast. These sightings were extremely brief and furtive because the sighter was running away as fast as he could go. Vague reports identified the beast as a bear. Half man and half bear. Always he was glimpsed at that spot down by the creek.

Initially, courting couples parked at that creek could feel their buggy gripped, raised off the ground, and jostled. If a buggy or wagon was left empty, it was smashed against a tree or slung high enough to break to pieces when it hit the ground. One man declared that he saw broken treetops damaged by a heavy object like a buggy or wagon thrown up there. Whatever object left in this area overnight wound up flung in the creek, slung into the treetops, or stomped into the ground. All of which required brute force that no human possessed.

Parents scared their children into quick obedience by references to ol' Maar.

Daredevil boys drug heavy junk objects into ol' Maar's domain to evaluate his response. Occasionally they hid in the perimeter to watch. But always ol' Maar detected their presence and his avalanche-like response sent them scattering for home.

Once the devilish boys tied a pet dog in the spot and left it for ol' Maar's amusement. After daylight they went to check. They heard the dog yammering before they arrived. They found it high up in a tree where the the dog's collar and leash had tangled in the branches, suspending it and leaving it clawing frantically for support to keep from choking.

In his milder all-man stages, ol' Maar could be approached by some of his former friends and contemporaries. Usually they had to over-power and restrain him. But they never could influence him to stop his vandalism. Once they said he broke down emotionally with sorrow and a desperate plea for forgiveness and help in his eyes. He told them old Tilda's evil spell made him do it. And he was powerless to stop.

They tried locking him in a solid room, but he almost beat himself to death, flailing at the walls. And when the moon got right, he and his beastly half could break through any wall. When they appealed to old Tilda to remove the spell, she flew into a massive rage and threatened to hex all of them. They even tried to locate another witch who might counteract the spell, but none would cooperate.

Ol' Maar solved the problem for them.

One fall morning, they found his body swinging by the neck from a rope over a tree limb. Did he take his own life? Or did he die at the hands of a lynching party composed of victims of his vandalism?

No one would claim the body. His family had long ago deserted him. The old country church wouldn't let him be buried in its cemetery. So they buried him at the spot down by the creek, and pushed up a few native slate rocks to mark the spot. Through the years various graffiti artists scratched crude words and images on the slate, including his name, ol' Maar.

"I heard 'em tell how he got his name," one old man recalled. "Some of the time he was half man and half bear. So, why not put the names together? The first two letters of man and the last two letters of bear. That makes M-A-A-R. That's what they called him from then on."

For a while vandalism stopped, and folks thought they had experi-enced the last of ol' Maar. But then it started again. The vandalism. Public and private. Deflated tires. Honey and beeswax dribbled over your windshield. Vulgar words and symbols spray-painted along the roads. Sugar in your gas tank. Outside water spigots left running. Booby-traps here and there. Lamps and lanterns blown out and emptied of oil. Mule harnesses mutilated. Firewood waterlogged. Straw hats full of wasps. Water snakes left in the horse-watering trough. Drying apples swept off the outbuilding roof.

All, and much more, attributed to the ghost of ol' Maar.

"The ghost was as bad or wuss than old man Ransom Barley after he was hexed," an oldster said. "You'd think the hex would be gone when a hexed person dies. But not this 'un. This ghost is hexed just as bad as ol' Ranse was. How do you transfer a hex like this from a real person to a ghost? We don't understand."

Nor do a lot of other people.

About the same time Ransom passed away, old Tilda Sammers died without ever releasing him or his ghost from the spell she cast.

So far no reports have come forth about any big misdeeds in that spot down by the creek where the beast, or half beast, joins the activity. Maybe the beast refuses to team up with a ghost, and is waiting until he, himself, becomes a ghost to participate.

Which won't be long if Uwharrians ever get him in their sights.

Meantime, if you or anyone you know can unhex a ghost, please come to the Uwharries.

To be safer, don't come when the moon is full.

GRANDFATHER'S GHOSTS

My grandfather claimed he had pet ghosts all around his farm home and outbuildings in central North Carolina's Uwharrie Mountains. He cautioned us visiting boys not to get too noisy and rambunctious lest we frighten the ghosts away, which we didn't want to happen. We didn't think much about it then, just accepted it. If Grandfather said he had pet ghosts around the homeplace, we believed him. So we toned down our bedlam. We didn't want to scare away his ghosts.

But *pet* ghosts? Ghosts so domesticated that they could be easily frightened? By humans? Pet ghosts so tame they were almost afraid of the dark?

That's what my grandfather claimed.

Now I find myself laughing at this incongruous concept. I do not laugh at the results he achieved with it, because it worked for him.

"You boys don't live here, so you can't understand the ghosts as well as I can," he said when we asked if he could trot out his pets for our entertainment. But he did the next best thing. He took us on a tour of their ghostly lair. Sometimes the ghosts could be heard moving about in the hayloft of the old log barn, or clinking the trace chains and creaking the leather on the mules' work harness. They caused the mules to snort and whinny, the chickens to mutter and squawk on the roost, the old hound dog to bark and howl at the moon, and the screech owls to act up. Grandfather said if you listened closely you could hear lots of other ghostly sounds: cornshucks ripping apart and fat ears colliding around the corncrib, wheat being stirred in the granary bins, the corn sheller activating, assorted rustling sounds on the roof, rasping and clawing on the walls of the older outbuildings as if a ghost had forgotten he could go through walls and, trapped now, was trying to find a way out.

Although we tried on every visit, my cousins and I could never pin down a ghost–that is, definitely see or hear or feel or touch a ghost–the way Grandfather claimed he could. We asked him why.

"You got to live with 'em, right close in among 'em, day and night, year after year," he explained. "And these old buildings, they're a refuge—the older the better." A week was as long as we ever stayed at Grandfather's, not nearly long enough to win any ghostly companionship. So we tried another approach.

We pestered Grandfather into letting us accompany him, usually one of us at a time, on his late afternoon chores, during which he visited most of the ghostly lairs. But it was disappointing. No ghosts performed. "They know you're here and they don't like it," Grandfather whispered. "They resent a stranger. You're intruding. They won't do anything but sulk with you here."

Although we never saw a live demonstration, Grandfather told us how he used his pet ghosts.

Occasionally after dark he'd forget if he had secured a door or gate, and he'd saunter off into the black night without flashlight or lantern. When he got to the desired spot, click, a blob of ghostly light illuminated the area well enough for him to do what was needed. This blob-of-light ghost also hovered over lost cows and mules, enabling Grandfather to find them easily. "That's 'Loomie'. He 'luminates things for me," he said.

Another ghost he called "Windy". Windy blew in his face and woke him at night if there was smoke, fire, or malfunction around the house, or if there were any prowlers or problems outside. "Better'n a guard dog," he said.

"Handy" was his nickname for the pet ghost who found lost hammers, nails, and tools; who helped him accomplish two-man tasks that were impossible for Grandfather alone; and who saved him from many a scrape, blister, or spill. Once he tried to move a dilapidated wooden corn planter to make some repairs. It wouldn't budge. He tried to run his hand underneath to discover the problem, but his hand wouldn't go. Abruptly he found himself on his knees with his head bent low. He looked under the planter and saw a large wasp nest. Had he rammed his hand under there it would have been covered with stinging wasps. "Handy was looking out for me then, too," he said.

Another ghost specialized in just one task—helping Grandfather turn the windlass handle when they were drawing up a heavy bucketful of water from deep in the old dug well.

Chickens ran loose around the premises. Laying hens made their own nests in and around the barn and outbuildings. When he came up short gathering eggs, Grandfather knew the hens had stolen a new nest, and he started searching. This is where the "Cackle" ghost came in. When Grandfather approached exasperation in his futile search, this ghost cackled softly and kept cackling until it led him to the new nest.

There were others. "Ornery" was the playful ghost who enjoyed pulling innocent pranks on Grandfather. The barn ghost lured visitors to the hayloft and disoriented them so badly they required assistance getting down. Ol' "Squealer" called the hogs in for feeding before Grandfather was ready. And "Tinkletoes" sounded like he or she was tiptoeing up close to whisper in your ear.

I remember that Grandfather always paid close attention to little things. He noticed when the old mule twitched her pointed ears and swished her tail in a new way; when raindrops pattered or pounded on the tin roof; when dust eddied up in front of the barn; when the mockingbird or cicadas stopped singing abruptly; when hinge or floorboard creaked; when a spider web loomed large on a dewy morn; when the wind moaned around the eaves, lashed the tree branches, or flopped a piece of loose tin; when frost weeds, heavy and fat, tilted over and nodded; when cloud panoramas decorated the sky; when the fresh air became spiced with mysterious aroma. Clearly he understood, interpreted, and integrated these things.

To me, now, his pet ghosts were more guardian angels than ghosts. But he called them his pet ghosts. To this day I don't dispute Grandfather. Frequently I wish I had asked more questions, talked to and accompanied him more, and tried to understand his lifestyle better. Always I marvel anew at the peculiar circumstances, earthly and divine, that produce an individual so attuned that he generates his own phalanx of pet ghosts who automatically do his bidding.

Today I live in a seventy-five-year-old remodeled farmhouse, with outbuildings, on the fringe of the Uwharries where I try to cultivate a few pet ghosts of my own. I'm learning to appreciate my grandfather's ways, especially his concern that his pet ghosts not be disturbed by noisy boys. When the grandchildren visit, their antics shake and rattle the old house. Giving them the silence signal, I retreat to a quiet corner and implore my pet ghosts, if any are left, to be patient. The bedlam will subside.

If your surroundings and your lifestyle permit, you might want to consider this method of control and utilization. It's beginning to work for me—thanks to Grandfather.

(reprinted with permission from the October 1998 issue of *Our State* magazine)

THE REVOLT

The revolt started from restlessness among the occupants of an abandoned cemetery beside a lonely backroad on the far side of the Uwharries. Ghosts from the dozen or two graves became more and more agitated as the years passed. Nobody maintained the cemetery anymore. Hardly anyone visited it. Passersby on the old road threw litter on the graves. Occasionally a vandal knocked over one of the unsophisticated markers. Rascally boys even built a campfire in the cemetery one night, and let the fire burn over most of the graves. What the resident ghosts wanted, unanimously, was some attention, respect, companionship with the living—deliverance from the abandonment and desecration intensifying upon them by the local public and their uncaring survivors.

One day a motor vehicle knocked off on the old road adjacent to the cemetery. While the driver fiddled with the engine, his wife and children browsed through the cemetery, to the delight of the ghosts. Later another car approached and the ghosts concentrated on it. It, too, coughed and sputtered and quit adjacent to the cemetery. The occupants strolled among the graves and read the inscriptions on the markers. The ghosts rejoiced.

Then the ghosts discovered they could disable and stop vehicles anytime they wanted—just by concentration. They had a ghostly field day, much to the annoyance of the motorists. The ghosts exulted in this vastly increased live visitation. Drivers summoned mechanics and tow trucks. But nobody could find anything wrong with the stranded vehicles. After a while the engines started and the vehicles operated again, leaving the owners extremely puzzled.

Thrilled at this temporary satisfying of their craving for attention, the ghosts considered an intriguing idea. Could they use the same technique to generate more, bigger and wider attention upon themselves and their kindred?

A leader rose from their ranks and quickly expanded this idea.

Burt Romero Plankton united all his counterparts in the little cemetery. Their mounting unrest led to activism, then to crusading, then to revolt, one with consequences no one believed could ever happen. Legions of ghosts from everywhere joined them. All were determined to be heard and have their cause addressed, because they had a legitimate complaint, a classic class-action case of discrimination.

A transplanted Northerner, Burt had died suddenly. Then, just as quickly, his family cremated him and buried his ashes, unceremoniously, in the little cemetery near where he lived in the Uwharries. Some folks said he died of emotional stress and moodiness. Even after twenty years of residence, he, being a stranger and a Yankee, was never fully accepted by the Uwharrie people. He was just tolerated. Then he rested peacefully for a few years before the uprising started, which led to his leadership role in the revolt.

Burt set the stage in his capsuled description of the initial complaint, widely and instantly circulated through all the spectral channels.

"Dammit, I was discriminated against when I died and most people dying around then and ever since have been, too," he groused into the apparitional network. "We didn't have a wake. Our family—nobody—gave us a wake. We want a wake, we want justice. We want a rollback. We want to be recognized. We want compensation. We want wake!"

This message and variations, plus elaborations, went to every ghost in the country. Then it went overseas and became a global cause celebre which leaders could not ignore.

Burt's elaboration won over all the apathetic ghosts and turned them into passionate spearheaders.

When he came to live near his wife's people in the Uwharries twenty years ago, Burt said, it was the custom in just about every family to give the deceased a wake. No matter how the person died—natural causes, suicide, accident, homicide, feuding, brawl, duel, whatever—he deserved a wake. And most people got it.

By the time family members and neighbors had washed, dressed, and prepared the body for burial, the menfolk had built a pinebox coffin for displaying the corpse. Progress slowly crept in when undertakers came and took the body to their establishment for embalming, then brought it back in a coffin for display in the family home. Usually the display space was the front room, or parlor, of the home, which the womenfolk had scrubbed down and tidied to perfection. Often in addition to flowers, a memento, an object closely identified with the deceased, would be placed on or adjacent to the open coffin.

The vigil usually occurred on the second night after death when everything was in order and the news had circulated throughout the community.

At least two people sat up all night long with the corpse. Sometimes they alternated in two or three-hour shifts. Occasionally one pair would stay until midnight, the second pair until daylight. These corpse-sitters usually were volunteers, often good friends of the deceased. Never did the weather get too rough or the inside activity too boisterous to displace these official corpse-sitters. Nor did they interfere with the goings-on. They made sure no one bothered the star of the show or ran off with him or anything of value pertinent to him.

The festivities began a while after dark and continued until the wee hours, often attracting scores of friends, relatives, acquaintances, and well wishers. Younger people came primarily for the partying and socializing. Everyone enjoyed the music, dancing, games, food, and reminiscing about the dearly beloved departed. Often the wake brought the best musicians, the best singers and dancers, the best square dance caller, the best short speechmaker who infrequently halted the fun to pay a brief oratorical tribute to the deceased. Another big magnet for the men was a jar of moonshine cleverly positioned outside the house somewhere.

Sometimes the family exercised its option for a second night of wakeful activities honoring the dead.

All this is what Burt referred to in his elaboration.

Most of his fellow ghosts already were knowledgeable about wakes and realized how much they had missed. Instantly they rallied to the cause.

"Of course, we want wake," they chorused. "We were left out. Forgotten. Denied. Discriminated against. We want a recall, another chance. We want wake. And we want it retroactive for each year since we died."

Those few ghosts, the more recent ones, who didn't know about wakes were quickly educated and indoctrinated into the revolt.

There were a few diehards who wouldn't join the revolt, however, and held out for neutrality. These anti-wakers were led by ol' iconoclastic Titus Fruholt, who was against everything in life and after life.

"In twenty years wakes faded away around here and probably everywhere," Burt elucidated. "No more wakes. How sad. How totally unacceptable. Wakes have been held for hundreds of years, probably for thousands of years. And now, no more? Outrageous! We can't stand for it. We gotta have wakes. We want wake. That's our battle cry. The three W's. We want wake!"

Why did wakes fade away?

"Careless people. Indifferent people. They let it happen. Right before our eyes. Another casualty in the erosion of our rights and freedom. Some say it was inevitable. Progress. Technology. Sophistication. Cultural advances. Hell! The funeral home people replaced it with what? What do they call it—family visitation night? Pack everything into an hour or two. How does that honor the dead? How? Me? I felt like I was impaled naked on a high pedestal somewhere and not being honored, just gawked at by a long line of loonies. I was a victim of modern expediency and efficiency. I was robbed. I was short-changed. I suffered indecent discrimination. I was taken advantage of. But now I know better. So I want justice. I want it retroactive. I want wake!"

Recognizing his rough edges and inadequate diplomacy, Burt gradually relinquished his leadership role to Sal Moany. In life a Philadelphia lawyer who went through the quick crematorium to ashes to spreading routine, Sal automatically took over and became one of ghostdom's finest front and point men. It was a cause to his liking. Through instantaneous communication, he organized ghosts border to border, coast to coast. He laid out some strategy.

Out of courtesy and respect, Sal checked in with Burt from time to time.

"We have unlimited personnel," Sal said. "We're about ready. Before long we'll have one or more pro-waker ghosts shadowing and lobbying every lawmaker of any consequence in this entire nation. Every representative and senator in Washington, D.C., every city, town, and county of any size. Every individual of stature or political clout. All media. We've got 'em sown up already. We'll whisper in their ear, hang our slogan around their neck, make 'em hold placards, cause our pictures, ads, and news stories to appear on every screen, broadcast, bulletin, and periodical. Easy to coordinate. Easy to accomplish. We've got 'em by the balls!"

The time came to lay out some detailed demands. Sal consulted with ghostdom's top strategists.

All agreed—it's got to be simple, reasonable, and binding.

First and foremost, we want to be recognized. Let's start with the proactive part.

Let's give all families, churches, and funeral homes throughout America one year to make amends. One year to provide a wake for all the deceased who wanted a wake but didn't get it during the past generation. Say the past thirty-three years. As well as for all those ghosts who have changed their minds in retrospect and would now like a wake. All such ghosts will cooperate fully. Funeral homes will provide names and dates. Families can provide obituaries, pictures, and mementos. Church cemeteries, plus all public and private burial grounds, will be open for documentation.

These retroactive wakes can be commemorative in format. That is, scaled down somewhat from the heyday wake. Also they can be held individually or en masse. It's up to the family. En masse is recommended. This way, each community or church can hold just one big wake to serve all its unwaked deceased during the past generation. The en masse wakes can be held in the church, fellowship hall, community building, school auditorium, football stadium, municipal park, lodge hall, or down by the river.

The en masse wakes must be all-inclusive, requiring exhaustive research and compilation skills from the sponsors, so no deserving ghost is left out.

Will the ghosts materialize during this long overdue wake in their honor? It's entirely up to the ghost. Some will materialize and participate in the dancing and feasting. Others will remain invisible wallflowers. Names should be posted, perhaps even called out, during the festivities. All genuine aspects of the old-time wakes should be represented in the modern version. But no long-winded speeches. No gratuitous oratory.

What about continued recognition?

Here comes Wake Day!

Since Halloween already is synonymous with ghosts, make Halloween take on double duty as National Wake Day, honoring all unwaked ghosts, past, present, and future. This will require an act of Congress to pass a proclamation declaring October 31 as National Wake Day, comparable to Flag Day, Memorial Day, Veterans Day, Labor Day, etc. The proclamation will suggest appropriate observation activities locally and nationally. Everyone is encouraged to observe this national holiday in reverent tribute to our dead.

Implementation is ongoing.

Sal and his strategists produced a tentative proclamation. Ghosts whispered in the ear and consciousness of all Congressmen, key officials, and lobbyists. Unaccountably the media publicized this movement. However, once it became public, the ghostly proposal generated ridicule and derision. Congress acted predictably–rejection and dismissal. An absurdity. Beneath its dignity. Hide it forever in a committee.

This flat rejection angered Sal, Burt, and legions of ghosts.

"We will have to be a bit more assertive," Sal said. "We'll give them a deadline."

The ghosts gave the government one month to act favorably on their proposal, to declare October 31 as National Wake Day, an official holiday from now on into perpetuity.

If this deadline was not met, something drastic and interesting would happen throughout America. Something that would get your attention. We will not tell you what. Be sure you understand–we mean business!

Reluctantly, messengers brought the ghostly threat to the attention of the President of the United States. He huddled briefly with his advisors and key people. All were negative. All advised him to ignore the threat as preposterous and unreal.

"We'll be laughed at forever if we give any credence to an absurd demand like that," they told him. "Communication from the other side? From the dead? That's unscientific. That's superstition and witchcraft. That's worse than the lunatic fringe. Forget it completely. Let's get on to weightier matters."

A month passed without any further consideration.

At 12:01 a.m. the following day, something drastic happened throughout America.

All screens went down and refused to function. *All* screens. They could not be reactivated.

Movie screens. Television screens. Computer screens. Even laptops. Even built-ins and portables. No matter the size or the complexity, every screen refused to light up and function normally. Everywhere, too. From hospitals to universities, skyscrapers to basement ghettos, Wall Street to the Pentagon, metropolis to hamlet, battleship to jetliner, private home to nursing homes and prisons.

After an hour of monotony, the screens began changing a little. Against a muggy gray background, a profile began to appear on the screens. Little by little. Then it became obvious. A head and neck profile of Sal! Then a similar one of Burt! Their misty, wraith-like profiles filled most of the screens. No emotion. Completely expressionless. At intervals they alternated, blank screen, then the profiles.

Occasionally contrasty letters crawled across the bottom of the screen: WE WANT WAKE.

Sometimes the words were followed by a signature: Pro-wakers of America. Or Pro-wakers of USA. Or just PWO USA.

Bedlam resulted. Nationwide chaos. It affected the remainder of the world. Practically everything shut down. Government, too. Manufacturing, transportation, utilities, communication, the military, medical facilities. Everything electronic involving a screen refused to work. The glitches were permanent, unfathomable, worse than any virus, worse than any hacker ever dreamed of.

Hardships were reported. More came in constantly in increasing volume. Something had to be done.

Officials high and low cried frantically for relief. No one knew what to do. Emergency and security personnel went on standby to help the locally distressed. But a permanent solution evaded all the experts.

How do you free up, nationwide, all the locked up, clogged up, glitched up, frozen screens and channels?

By mid-morning the President re-huddled with his top advisors. All were stressed out, wailing and agonizing over the nation's failure to find a solution to this unprecedented problem.

"We're past the critical stage," a top advisor moaned. "We're suffering terribly. Our whole nation is. The world soon will be. If this keeps up much longer, the carnage will be worse than from a nuclear war."

Someone remembered the month-old warning from the pro-waker ghosts.

"Contact their spokesman and let's renegotiate," the President ordered.

A dozen hands went scurrying toward telephones and intercoms.

A voice said, "No need for frenzy or panic. I'm already here. I'm ready to negotiate."

A roomful of startled people quieted down. Everyone turned. Guards drew their weapons. Extra barricades slid into place at the doors and windows.

From a big television screen on one side of the room, Sal spoke from his expressionless profile: "Settle down. Take it easy. Make yourselves comfortable. Let's talk a bit. What can I do, or what can *we* do, to help?"

An advisor rose to respond, but the President waved him down and took over.

"Tell us what has happened," he said.

"What has happened is what we told you would happen a month ago if you ignored our demand to make October 31 National Wake Day," Sal replied. "You did ignore it—a simple and reasonable request—so this is the result. You brought it upon yourselves and your nation."

"What is it?" the President asked.

"Ectoplasm," Sal explained. "A special substance, and weapon, unique to us ghosts and kindred spirits. We can use it, place and control it, locally or globally, at a moment's notice. Discontinue it the same way. In this application, we have deployed it to jam and clog up all your electronic freeways, all your broadcasting, transmitting and receiving facilities; also to block your screens. It is invisible, undetectable, and impenetrable. Nothing you have will touch it or budge it."

A circle of gasps fluttered around the room.

"How long will it last?" the President asked.

"Twenty-four hours," Sal said. "Which means we have better than twelve hours to go. I will stop it tonight at midnight. No damage will have been done, equipment-wise. Everything will be normal after that."

"Can't you stop it sooner? Right now?"

"Yes."

"Will you?"

"No."

"Why not?"

"We don't like being ignored."

"All right, all right!" The President's voice rose. "We won't ignore you. You've got our attention. We will negotiate. Now let's call off this—this—ecto nonsense right now."

"Midnight," Sal replied sternly.

"Listen, you—you—" the President sputtered, "you have caused horrendous problems. Unimaginable shut downs and complications. Hardships are mounting. People are suffering. We want this stopped right now."

"Midnight," Sal repeated.

Once more the President tried: "Please call it off. This is the worst crisis ever to hit our nation. Technologically speaking we're in shambles. I'm pleading with you. Please end it right now. Please!"

"Midnight," Sal said nonchalantly.

The President threw up his hands and sat.

"I'll shoot the bastard!" a guard snarled, leveling his high-powered automatic weapon at the television.

"No!" several advisors yelled.

"Okay," one said to Sal. "Let's talk. What do you want us to do?"

"Make October 31 National Wake Day. Make it official. Through all the normal channels and procedures. Have the President proclaim it. Releases to all the media. Kick it off with one big observation in

Washington, D.C. Have all that pomp and razzle-dazzle. Some of our distinguished alumni will attend and monitor everything."

"How much time have we got?"

"A month from midnight."

"And if we can't—if we don't meet this deadline, then what?"

"More ecto," Sal answered. "We'll clog all your channels, all the satellite networks, and throw away the key. We'll keep all your screens blank indefinitely."

After a brief huddle, the advisor came back and said, "Okay, we'll try and meet your demands. The President has agreed. We think we can do it. Now, that's settled. Let's seal it in good faith by removing the ecto and freeing up our networks."

For the first time Sal's profile moved. His head nodded. "At midnight."

The profile vanished, replaced by a slowly roiling muggy mass of gray. Ectoplasm?

*   *   *

Precisely at midnight, all screens jumped back to life, all channels and networks opened, and all electronic circuitry worked normally again.

*   *   *

Half the month passed with no developments.

"They're working on it," Sal reported to Burt. "We've got 'em under surveillance every moment. Just a few more days."

But another problem arose. Surveillance revealed growing opposition to National Wake Day among groups of anti-wakers. They became more vocal and reached into higher levels of the political stratosphere with their promise to counteract any threat from the pro-wakers. Government hierarchy rapidly cultivated an alliance with these dissenters. Would they, could they, jeopardize the pro-wakers' National Wake Day movement and its imminent success at this late day?

"Titus Fruholt has organized the dissenters," Sal said to Burt. "He's a lifelong and ghostlong troublemaker and agitator. Always against everything. Always derailing and throwing up roadblocks. Never happy unless he's neck deep in subversive controversy. He's articulate, too. A paranoid egomaniac. If I had him in the courtroom, I'd castigate him until his ears fell off. But we've got to deal with the rascal now, somehow."

They mulled it over with some of the other strategists.

"Titus is trying to sell the government on some wild scheme that he can protect them from our ecto," Sal said. "Claims he can control it better than we can. That he has an antidote for it. That he can clear it just as fast as we can apply it. We know he has no such ability. He's fantasizing. His main goal is upstaging us, but he will hoo-doo the government. We can't let him get away with it.

"Burt, I've got my hands full in Washington. How about you monitoring Titus. Find a way to subdue him. Neutralize him. Muzzle him some way. If nothing else works, overdose him on ecto. That'll keep him sedated until after the deadline."

Burt disguised himself and closed in on Titus, who rabbleroused with a group of anti-wakers. Immediately Titus sensed his presence. "An enemy within our gates," his thin voice railed. "An impostor. No, a spy. Spies are shot. But we won't shoot this one. We'll convert him. Make him see the light. Let him know that we have the upper hand. While we are in the minority, we have a secret power that puts us in control. We are, in a global sense, the tail wagging the dog. Your National Wake Day plan is doomed, brother. We are striking a deal with the government which puts us in control and puts you pro-wakers back in the grave where you belong, and keeps you there forever."

Titus ranted on about the superiority of his group. They were brainwashing government officials. They had perfected an antidote for ectoplasm. They had hatched a plan for takeover—worldwide—through a super secret global ghostly conspiracy. They had tapped into a heretofore unknown segment of ghostdom, an elite conclave of ghostly geniuses whose combined intelligentsia could be instantaneously harnessed and focused in any direction with immediate observable results. He called it UGG: Universal Genius Ghosts. And—ha, ha, ha—he alone had the key to the tapping-in procedure.

Recoiling at this sinister news, Burt tried all his traditional deterrent techniques on Titus. None worked. Titus had turned into a madman. He had to be stopped. How?

Quickly Burt reviewed his ghostly roster for expertise among his pro-waker colleagues.

Materializing from the multi-millions came Dr. Steph Mannville, an internationally famous scientist/philosopher who specialized in anesthesiology. Burt explained the pro-wakers' critical situation, and Dr. Steph agreed to help.

"Please hurry," Burt pleaded. "The deadline is right away and we've got a lot of work waiting."

Dr. Steph groused about never having anesthetized a ghost before, but he set to work. He said ecto could be used for anything, including anesthesia. Proportioning it was the critical factor. An improper dose would adversely affect the patient. Burt insisted that the doctor include some truth serum because he wanted to question Titus and learn the UGG tapping-in procedure. Unknown to Burt, the doctor experimented on a couple of anti-wakers before he was satisfied.

They isolated Titus and Dr. Steph made Burt leave. He wanted no witnesses to ghostkind's first anesthetization on a ghost. In a few moments he called Burt back. Titus was groggy, then comatose. A skilled hypnotist, Dr. Steph then de-programmed Titus, removing all his leadership abilities and leaving him almost inarticulate. "The overdose will keep him sedated and morose for weeks," he said.

With the truth serum apparently working, Burt and Dr. Steph questioned Titus progressively to the verge of revealing the UGG secret. Then Burt made Dr. Steph vacate. After more gentle prodding, Titus revealed the secret—a simple phrase, memorable, but simple. Burt filed it away for ghosts to use into perpetuity.

They rejoined Sal in Washington.

"I know you were successful," Sal said. "The anti-wakers are powerless without their leader. Most of them are joining up with us, anyway. I've already convinced the President's people they have no alternative. We're in control. They're ready to capitulate. Maybe tomorrow."

Next day the announcement came that Congress had approved National Wake Day. Television news highlighted it. Newspaper headlines blared it. Politicians and talk show hosts expanded and speculated on it. Investigative reporters tried to dig into the background and find out what precipitated the sudden creation of this new national holiday. But they didn't get very far, except to relate it, vaguely, to the recent unpleasantness with the unworking screens.

The President put his signature on the proclamation in a live ceremony at the White House on Halloween night, Washington, D.C. time. Following his brief remarks, a huge Wake Day parade, the first ever, filled the streets of downtown Washington, featuring float-sized renditions of classic ghosts throughout history, literature, and folklore.

Everyone was invited to come live or tune in to participate in this historic kick-off event officially launching National Wake Day.

The sudden creation of the newest holiday intrigued many Americans. They thought they could learn more about it if they came to the festivities in person. Millions of them did. So many that it swamped accommodations for hundreds of miles around.

Millions more came, too. But these millions caused no disruption. They were scarcely noticed; practically all of them remained invisible. Sal and Burt and scores more of their pro-waker counterparts could not resist attending. They hovered over and around the President and his entourage. A few of them materialized briefly, but caused no alarm, although the security people did scrutinize them strangely. You will not recognize them in printed pictures or on TV footage.

Editorialists and columnists said the crowd at the ceremony and the nearly-all-night parade was probably the largest assemblage ever in the history of the capital. Reporters remarked about the good behavior of the crowd, a remarkable unity, no vandalism, and hardly any litter left to pick up on the streets the next day.

"Everyone appeared to enjoy a memorable and positive experience at this historic event," one columnist wrote.

Said another: "The impression I got was rather strange. Each person seemed to enjoy soaking up all the action and atmosphere and telling himself something like this: 'When I get back home, I'm going to make our local officials observe National Wake Day next Halloween. This is great!'"

While their counterparts applauded, Sal smiled all the way back to Philadelphia. Dr. Steph smiled all the way back to Germany. Burt smiled all the way back to the Uwharries.

The restlessness is gone now. The ghost of Burt Romero Plankton enjoys tranquillity where his ashes are buried in the little cemetery in the Uwharries. Something remarkable happened to his headstone. An oval picture of him, smaller than the palm of your hand, appeared laminated and embedded in the top center of the marker. Nobody knows where it came from or who put it there. Likely his admiring friends from the ghostly spheres materialized his picture there permanently as a tribute to the man, or to the ghost, who started the revolt which led to the creation of National Wake Day.

This profile of Burt is an outstanding likeness. White shirt, contrasty tie, dark jacket. His facial features come through sharp and clear, including the glint in his eye.

If you look closely, you can see just a hint of amusement on his face.

NESSIE NEEDS A JACKET

Yes, Nessie does need a jacket! Few people realize the significance of these words today, but that was not the case many years ago in the Uwharries. Yes, the need continues–

Nessileen Mojave, a beautiful southern belle in her late teens from a wealthy plantation family, fell in love with Beemer Slack, a penniless boy from a poor tenant family.

It was hopeless from the start. Practically everyone knowledgeable about the situation knew it would never work out, mainly because of Nessie's father.

Sharpal Mojave had a fiery Spanish/Italian temper which exploded constantly. Conditions could only go one way–his way. He ruled overbearingly, browbeating and castigating those around him. In spite of his ego, he amassed large landholdings, farming and related enterprises, and considerable prestige. He wasn't about to let his daughter marry such a lowlife, a tenant farm boy.

The domineering father failed to recognize anything good about Beemer. Working at the farm chores, Beemer developed strength and athletic prowess, plus an amazing amount of energy and a desire to learn. He tried to persuade Nessie to leave her family and run away with him, but she could not do so.

The only time they could see each other, then only briefly, was when her father was away on a trip. Rarely could she leave the house undetected. Even more rarely could he gain entrance. Both became frustrated and moody.

Then Sharpal confined Nessie to the house under lock and key, never to be let outside unless he was there to supervise the outing. He went to Beemer's house and told him face to face that he would have the boy shot if he came around the Mojave house. All the plantation workers had been so instructed.

A few days later a pistol shot rang out in the Mojave home. They found Nessie dying in a pool of blood from a gunshot to the head, her finger still curled around the pistol grip. They buried her in a family cemetery, guarded by big oak trees, up beside the public road. Her grave occupied a spot just inside the wrought iron fence enclosing the small plot. Passersby on the road could easily see the grave through the fence.

On the day of the burial, Beemer stood on the back edge of the crowd. Tears rolled down his cheeks. He alternately looked at the casket and at Sharpal Mojave. Beemer knew that Sharpal held him responsible for his daughter's death. When he looked toward Beemer, the man's fierce eyes were full of hatred and vengeance.

Beemer wondered if he should leave and go far away from Sharpal Mojave and his threats. But no. He couldn't bear to leave the area where his beloved Nessie was buried. He determined to remain there to his dying day.

Months passed. Winter gripped the Uwharries with heavy frost, icy winds, and snow.

Early on a sub-freezing morning, passersby on the road spotted something strange on the fence at the Sharpal Mojave family graveyard.

A body was impaled on top of the wrought iron fence.

Word spread fast. A group gathered. Somebody called the constable and the preacher.

The body of Beemer Slack sprawled face down horizontally along the top of the wrought iron fence, exactly even with Nessie's grave.

Sharp spikes at the top of the fence had penetrated his body. One jabbed into his mouth and came out through the back of his head. Another went through the base of his neck, two more penetrated halfway through his stomach section. Dripping blood had frozen into a scarlet icicle reaching all the way to the ground. Only a thin, ragged shirt covered the upper part of the body. A torn section of the shirt flapped in the icy wind as if greeting the new arrivals who came to gawk.

Sharpal Mojave viewed the body. Folks said later that he snarled something like, "Good riddance."

Some men wondered if Sharpal could have slammed the body there on top of the fence, or had it done. Then they looked up and the method of Beemer's death became clear.

A large limb from one of the oak trees jutted over the fence, and over Nessie's grave. Bark on the big limb looked frazzled, like it had been freshly disturbed.

A viewer speculated: "Must be twenty feet or better up there. Beemer could have climbed that tree easy. He could shinny out that limb and lie on it and look down at Nessie's grave. Long as he wanted to. Nobody would ever know he was there."

Did he fall off the limb and onto the spikes of the fence accidentally? Or did he deliberately plunge himself off onto the fence to end his emotional agony? And to die at the grave of his beloved Nessie?

No one will ever know for sure.

Nor does anyone remember where they buried Beemer.

A long time passed before anything else of significance occurred at the Mojave family graveyard.

One chilly fall night, a farmer in his one-horse wagon returned home from a day at the cotton gin. When he passed near the graveyard, he saw an attractive young woman standing beside the road and imploring him to stop. He stopped. His mule snorted nervously. The thinly dressed woman approached closely. She was cold. She wanted to borrow a jacket. He could get it back the next day. The farmer removed his coarse jacket and handed it to her. She held the jacket and watched him as he drove away.

Next morning his jacket hung from a fence spike over Nessie's grave.

"It was Nessie," the farmer declared. "I know it was. I remember her."

After that a number of jackets and thick wraps were left hanging on the same spike following cold nights. Their lenders reclaimed them the next day, wondering how the garments had been utilized during the night.

Only on cold nights did the ghost of Nessie Mojave appear to people passing on the road and ask to borrow a warm garment. Rarely did any traveler refuse her request.

"How could you refuse to help her," asked an elderly female sympathizer. "That beautiful young woman, standing there, trembling in the cold night. So sincere. So polite. Thankful. No doubt about it. It was Nessie's ghost. Nobody's gonna say no to a pretty woman alone and freezing on a road at night. One man who didn't have a jacket or wrap went home and got one and brought it back to her."

Back then one point in the story generated lasting debate.

Did Nessie borrow the jacket for herself or for Beemer?

Most people, especially the women, opt for Beemer.

"Remember," one said, "Beemer died right there at that location. Violently, too. It was freezing weather. His shirt was thin and ripped to pieces. Sure, he was cold. His ghost is still cold and needs warming. So she borrows the jackets for him."

Time has eradicated the Mojave family cemetery and its fence. Nobody knows the location anymore.

If you're driving in the Uwharries on a cold night, and a beautiful young woman implores you to stop and loan her a jacket, please do so.

You can always recover it the next day at the same location.

JANE DIRK'S LIGHT

The preacher used to break down and weep as he told this story to his congregations in little country churches through the Uwharries. Before he finished, half the congregation sobbed, too.

"Which one do you want?"

These five words intensified the sobbing. Over the sanctuary, a woman or two, handkerchiefs to their faces, half rose as they shrieked in emotional pain, their arms raised, palms outward as if imploring the preacher to stop, because they couldn't take any more. Their anguish was overwhelming.

But the preacher wouldn't stop. He had a good thing going. He had their unflinching attention. He had to finish a good story, and this one well illustrated his sermon on love. He preached love. Transcending love. Those five words always cast the right spell.

*   *   *

Nine-year-old Tabitha Trenchet accompanied her father, Bascom Trenchet, to the blacksmith shop to get some cast iron plow shovels sharpened. The tumble-down shop provided darkened relief from the hot sun. Puffs of gray hair ballooned around the sweaty head and shoulders of the middle-aged smithy. His shoulders hunched a bit. His hands and feet were not as agile as a smithy's ought to be. Beneath feverish eyes, an expression of sorrow appeared chiseled on his flushed face.

In and around the wide entrance, four children played in the dust and splashed water on each other from a wooden barrel. The oldest, a boy about Tabitha's age, tried to help his father. The others ranged in age down to a two-year-old toddler. All wore soiled and patched clothing.

Finished with his work at the forge and anvil, the smithy pulled Bascom to one side and nodded to the four children. "Which one do you want?"

Tabitha heard those words and remembered them all her life. She also heard what else the emotional blacksmith said to her startled father.

"I gotta find homes for these children. Right away! I ain't got much time left. Since my wife, Jane, died a few months back, things have got wuss and wusser. Looking after these kids and myself is too much. I can hardly pick up a hammer. I'm too old and weak and sick to farm anymore. Can't even garden. I'm coughing and spitting up blood. Consumption, I reckon. The doc says I can't last but a few more weeks, if that long. The neighbors are helping some, but we're about to starve. All our clothes wore out, too. With winter coming on—I know I won't be here—I got to find a place for these kids. You got first choice. Which one do you want?"

Shocked, Bascom Trenchet mumbled that he would have to consult with his wife about taking a child. He hustled Tabitha into the buggy and switched the horse into a trot. At home he shared this news with his wife. She made him take food back to the family that very evening.

Next day the community rallied. Dan Dirk, the dying blacksmith, got the help he needed.

They found suitable homes for the oldest boy and girl. A youngish widow agreed to move into the Dirk home and look after the two younger children and their dying father. Sufficient food, clothing, and cash came in. Nearby farmers tilled the Dirk land, helped with the gardening and the domestic livestock. The children were able to visit each other occasionally.

Dan Dirk, the blacksmith, lived only a few days after the widow Sims joined the family. The neighbors buried him beside his wife in the little family plot in the edge of the yard.

The children thrived in their wholesome environment.

An excellent homemaker and manager, the widow Sims groomed the two younger children into model youngsters. Within a couple of years she invited the two older siblings to come back to their old home to live. The hosting families continued some support for a while. From then on, the four children, their home and grounds, and everything related became role models in the community. Credit went to the widow Sims, but she nonchalantly shrugged the credit away.

About then is when the ghost light began appearing.

They called it Jane Dirk's Light.

Along with it came a mysterious clanging in the old blacksmith shop, suddenly operative again after long neglect. They called it the Daniel Dirk Banging.

The light and clanging sometimes worked together, sometimes independently. Nobody knew when either would occur.

Most always the light appeared as a round ball of fire or illumination at the edge of a pine forest, near a creek and a natural spring where nearby residents obtained their drinking water and washed their clothes.

Before she died generations ago as an old woman, Tabitha Trenchet told tales about the Dirk ghosts which have been handed down by her descendants.

"That light appeared and bobbed along in the edge of the trees early at night, before bedtime," she said. "Everybody in the community saw it. Lots of times it was on rainy, foggy, misty nights when lots of moisture was in the air. Some people called it foxfire. But it weren't no such a thing. It was Jane Dirk's Light. That light was a sign, a symbol. It always meant something. You could count on that. A death in the community, an accident, somebody hurt, a fire, a drowning, somebody flooded out, a wedding, a new baby, an important visitor, something special. It never failed.

"Something else special about that light. Lots of folks believed it was Jane Dirk herself or her ghost coming back to minister to her children. Any crisis, big or little, brought her back. The mumps, whooping cough, measles, typhoid fever, chicken pox, the flu. She was right there helping look after those children. When they did something good at school or church, she was right there. She was the anchor and their close guide. The children learned to depend on her. This continued right on through school, through college, till they got established in good-paying jobs or professions. All of them did well in their later life."

That clanging in the blacksmith shop?

"It was Daniel Dirk. Everybody knew it. Nobody could see him, but they knew it was him. It was his hammering, his quality of work. He taught his eldest boy, Macon, how to do blacksmith work. That boy turned out good work, just like his daddy. Earned some money that way. No matter how busy, the work always got finished on time. Then that youngest boy, Ezro, did the same thing. Folks said ol' Daniel come back outta the grave and helped the boys at night. After all, he lay buried close by, so it was convenient. For her, too."

After all four Dirk children grew up, left home, and got established in careers, the widow Sims stayed on at the old home and looked after several other orphans who found their way into her care. She was buried there in the family cemetery near Jane and Daniel Dirk. In her later years, she shared some experiences, remembered and handed down by Tabitha Trenchet.

"Folks gave me the credit, but it certainly weren't all me," Tabitha quoted her as saying. "Not nearly all me. I couldn't, wouldn't-a done all that work looking after four kids full-time, along with all the house work, yard work, and gardening. Lordy, no. She helped me. Her, their mother. She did most of it. Oh, I know my way around the house and I can handle a kid or two. But all of them together? No way. I started out with two, remember? I coulda handled two. But not four. She brought the other two back here. She did it.

"And all them times at my wit's end. She came. She helped. She knew about it. I didn't have to beseech. She was there. In harvesting the vegetables and preserving them, I couldn't find this or that. Then it would turn up. Sewing up a dress for the girls or a shirt for the boys, I'd run out of thread or I'd need something or I'd forget how to do something, and, like magic, my problem was solved and everything worked out. Quickly, too.

"The way them children learned beat all. Amazing. Like a miracle. Yeah—*her* miracle. They learned fast. They did it all. All the house-work, all the skills and crafts, along with their studies and music and singing. The boys, too. They could do anything—patch the roof, land-scape the yard, cut the firewood, hitch the mule, help birth a calf, do all the blacksmith shop work. I didn't teach these kids all that so quickly. Their parents did. I *know* they did. I was with them night and day for years. I know what happened."

The widow Sims also told about another part of Jane Dirk's Light probably unknown to most people. Tabitha said the widow Sims told it this way:

"The Jane Dirk Light? Out there in the woods? Yes, I've seen it many a time. Most people around here did. And it meant something, too. But there was another Jane Dirk Light that nobody else ever saw. Just me and the children. It was her. You couldn't see her—just her light. Whenever she was in or around this house, you could see it, just a small circle of soft, golden light. Kinda like a halo, yet not a halo. We could see it in the house about everywhere. Anytime we needed anything, that light was there. When the children were asleep at night, that light hovered over their beds for a while. If they were sick or ailing, that light just about stayed there ministering to them. That light was full of energy. Healing energy. Sorta like a real person. Kind, gentle, peaceful. That light made you feel cheerful, serene, and secure. That light was love. A mother's love."

Today, no sign remains of the Dirk home place or graveyard. Nor of the stream, spring, or pine woods where people saw Jane Dirk's Light.

A big cultivated field covers it all. No one knows the exact location anymore. No one sees the light anymore.

At least, not the outside light.

*   *   *

The preacher ended his sermon with:

"That light of love still exists, my friends. You can see it everywhere. It will shine and glow forever. Because it's God's light. That's God's love a-shining through. It's ready to help us, all of us, right now, today and tomorrow. You don't have to be a child. You can be an adult, just as long as you are a child of God. And all of us are. Jane Dirk's Light was God's love expressed through a saintly mother. It works the same way through a father, brother, sister, grandparents, a teacher, friend, or neighbor. Get busy. Put it to use. Do it now. While you're alive. Now! Every time you smile or see a person smile, that's God's pure light a-shining through. Practice it. Please, practice it. If you're in need or if you see a need, call on God's love and light to come right now and help–just like it did through Jane Dirk's Light."

THE WHITE DEER

A ghost deer with whammy eyes used to appear in some of the wildest parts of the Uwharries. Some folks say this ghost of the albino buck is still here, although it might take a lot of looking to experience him today. Most informed people are satisfied to leave it that way.

Shrunk Batiford told why:

"It weren't me, now. Too long ago for that. But I've heard my pappy tell about what my grandpappy experienced with that ghost buck. Big scutter. Big, big! Lots bigger than any whitetail buck you'll ever see around here. Huge antlers. Solid white. Ghosty. Looked like a big white elephant or bull moose charging at ya. Nuthin' stopped 'im. You could shoot bullets into him all day and it didn't faze 'im. Trees didn't stop 'im. He'd run right through 'em. All you could do was try to get out of his way. But even that didn't work. 'Cause then he'd turn that evil eye on you. Nobody could stand that."

That evil eye was what zapped most people who encountered the ghostly white deer at close enough range.

Shrunk continued, "Grandpappy was out hunting for deer and wild turkey when he stopped in this pretty little cove on the side of a hill, way back deep in the woods. He saw the white buck coming toward him. He fired his musket—we've still got his old gun here—right into the middle of that big buck. It woulda killed any real live buck, but not this 'un. He kept coming. Grandpappy leaped up on a big rock, then scrambled up a steep rocky ledge and stood on top where the buck couldn't get to him. He thought he'd have time to reload and shoot again, but he didn't. That's when the buck's eye got 'im.

"Now I ain't no expert. I don't know nuttin' about special eyes. Just what I heard, what Grandpappy told. He said the buck's eyes got bigger and brighter. Turned kinda greenish, some yellow, gold and fire in it. Then it flashed out in a ray or beam, all the way to him. He felt it hit 'im. Sorta set him on fire inside all over. Don't know what it was. Nobody does. Magic, I guess. Anyway, it knocked 'im out. Out cold. He slumped over in them rocks and leaves. Musta laid there an hour or two before he came around.

"When he woke up, it was awful. Said he never felt wuss in his whole life. Sorta like coming around after a long drunk. He was mixed up and confused. Sore and aching all over. Stomach naw-see-ated. Eyes blurry. Trembling. Unbalanced and a little dizzy. Weak, headaches, and thirsty. He managed to crawl around and find his gun, then he hightailed it for home and never came back."

Hikers and hunters reported similar experiences in various parts of the Uwharries. In most cases they saw the white deer from a distance. Nobody wanted to get close enough to activate its evil eye.

That's been true ever since.

Speculation continues about the origin of the white deer. No facts emerge, just suppositions buried under layers of legend.

Back when Indians occupied the paradisiacal Uwharries, they hunted and fished and foraged just enough to sustain themselves without overtaxing the land. The land supported them and they took care of it as excellent stewards. Harmony existed between these Native Americans and all wildlife, plant life, the weather, and mother nature.

One village ran low on its meat supply. The elders told three young braves to go into a new part of the Uwharries, kill a big buck, and bring it back to the village for processing and eating. Seizing this assignment as a way to prove their manhood, the three young braves eagerly traveled more than a day's journey into the forested hills. They stopped and camped for the night at an idyllic cove on a hillside where a spring of pure water gurgled from a crevice in the rocky ledge.

Next morning a large white buck ambled into the cove. The braves immediately killed it with their spears and arrows. Elated at this prize, they hurriedly field-dressed the buck, tied it upside down to a pole, and lugged it back home to the acclaim of their hungry villagers.

But the old chief had misgivings about killing and eating a white deer. Such an animal was most unusual and special. Only a very few people ever got to see a white deer. It had mystery and intrigue about it. The chief feared that the gods had created and commissioned it, and now those gods were angry at its demise.

Two years passed, during which the village experienced increasing bad luck. Drought seared the land. Crops failed. Wild fruits and nuts were harder to find. Hunting and fishing proved unsuccessful. More babies died than usual.

The chief and the elders held a council. They attributed the bad luck to the death of the white deer. The three young braves would have to be punished.

The chief banished them from the village. He ordered the three braves back to the cove where they had slain the white deer. There they would remain for the rest of their lives, guarding the cove against all intruders and preserving it as a sanctuary for white deer. All three died there, with their weapons and valuables beside them.

The sacred cove lay undisturbed for generations. Shrunk's grandpappy was one of the first white men to venture into it.

Those who experienced the cove told strange tales.

One hunter said he must have got too close to the cove, because an Indian brave met him and motioned for him to turn around and go back. He said the brave appeared to be fully armed with a spear, a knife, and a bow and arrow.

Another hunter reported a similar encounter, except two braves accosted him, one on either side. This time, one of the braves appeared to have a rifle. Outnumbered, the hunter didn't challenge them. He turned and left.

Still another hunter faced the guardian ghost braves. He decided to ignore them. He lingered a bit then advanced.

"All of a sudden this huge white buck stood there, looking at me with them evil eyes," he said. "I tried to turn and go back, but before I could, that greenish beam hit me and it was all over. I was out like blowing out a candle. I stayed out for hours. When I come to my senses, I crawled and staggered out of them woods and I never could remember where it happened."

There was some talk of a small group of gypsies wandering into the cove and never coming out again.

Nobody knows where this sacred cove is anymore, so you could encounter the three guardian ghost braves anywhere in the Uwharrie woods. The advice is just to turn and go back.

Others say the ghosts of the gypsies help guard the cove, and that it's possible to hear faint strains of their inimitable music on blustery nights when the moon is full.

And if you're lucky enough to spot an albino buck in the Uwharrie woods, don't get close enough that he can zap you with his evil eye.

IN THE HEREAFTER

When the Mortimer family members came back to the Uwharries after a long absence, no one could believe that they brought a ghost with them. Apparently they did. Maybe not exactly. Maybe they activated a ghost that was already here, a ghost that still makes his presence known in subtle ways. Were it not for this subtlety, the story of Esther Mortimer and Eppie Taft would have faded into the limbo generations ago.

Esther and Eppie lived a mile apart, he near the bluff on Ribbon Creek, she on a big farm near the Stiles Orchard. She came from a prosperous and prominent family. His was non-existent. His mother died when he was born; his father died in an accident when Eppie was a youngster, after teaching the boy the basics of the stone mason trade. Living with an aged aunt proved unsatisfactory. She soon died and Eppie came back to the isolation of his shack in the woods. There he immersed himself in learning to work with stone.

They met one day when Eppie walked far down the creek, looking for a better place to quarry native slate which he had begun to use in making grave markers. Esther walked to the creek to enjoy the cool tranquillity. They quickly fell madly in love and rendezvoused at the creek several times a week. One day Esther's father followed her and ended the relationship, warning the young man never to come near his daughter again. Desperate, Eppie went to the Mortimer home, trying to see and communicate with Esther. Never did he succeed. Her parents waved him away, warned him sternly, even threatened him. Esther could not leave her home unchaperoned.

Finally Mrs. Mortimer took her daughter to Tennessee to live with relatives. Eppie knew nothing about how to get to far-off Tennessee. Heartbroken, he vented his frustration by working night and day, turning gray slate into beautiful grave markers.

Stacks of raw slate, ready to refine and process, surrounded his cabin and shop, which were deep in the woods. Eppie quarried the slate at a bluff on the creek bank, and hauled it by mule and wagon. His chisel and hammer became expert at finding the tiniest seams and layering this native stone into any thickness. Then his hand tools shaped it into almost any design he desired. His artistic etching made the inert slab of stone jump to life with names, dates, brief words, and symbols.

The top edge of the marker he could finish straight-line flat, or rounded like a half-moon, beveled edged, fluted, pointed like an arrowhead, rainbowed, serrated, waved, ribbed, or ruffled. Even shouldered and shined on by the sun.

Designs and symbols fascinated Eppie, and he excelled at creating objects like a Bible, open or closed, angels of many descriptions, a great shining light, sun rays, a dove, a halo, praying hands, crosses, an olive branch, a lamb, a cherub, a staff, a heart, a rose, a bowed head, a container of water. He carved these symbols into the stone itself, and displayed them prominently near the top center. Brief Bible verses and messages he centered beneath the names and dates.

Upon a death in the community, usually Eppie could pull a marker out of the stock to suit the family. Then all he needed were the names, dates, and the salutation. Erection he left to the family, although he would install the marker if pressed.

Most customers gave Eppie a few dollars. Others left garden produce or a slab of cured meat, or helped repair his chimney or take his old mule to the blacksmith for shoeing. A word of appreciation for his craftsmanship always satisfied him.

Eppie seemed to know when a death was imminent in the area. Some say he went ahead and etched the names and death dates, waiting only for the family to complete the information. Others said he could predict deaths so accurately that he had the markers completed beforehand. It gave rise to speculation—did he hasten deaths by so doing?

He gave special attention to two markers which he completed and set aside. Hardly anyone saw them.

The tops of both were heart-shaped. One contained the name of Esther Mortimer and the birth date, the space for the death date left blank. Down below were etched these words: "In the Hereafter." But the most striking feature was a pair of eyes, feminine eyes, staring at you from near the top center. Friendly and filled with expression, these eyes communicated a feeling of love. The longer you stared at them, the stronger this message became. Almost to the point of mesmerization.

A similar marker, also exquisitely done, contained Eppie's name, birth date, the same message, and a pair of piercing male eyes, staring straight out at the observer with strange sensitivity.

A few years passed during which Eppie's grave marker production never slackened. No one could fathom the reason for this vast overproduction.

One day Eppie disappeared. Nobody ever saw or heard from him again. No one found any trace of his whereabouts. A neighbor, Eppie's closest acquaintance, searched his shack and shop to no avail. The neighbor found the two special markers, but he left them concealed where they were.

There was speculation.

At the slate quarry on the creek bank, the neighbor noted a huge slab of rock had scaled off and fallen over in the creek, diverting part of the stream flow under and around one end. The shoulder-deep water covered about a third of the massive hunk of slate. Was Eppie's body pinned underneath? Could he have loosened the slate deliberately and let it fall on him? Why? Most people in the community knew about his heartbreaking experience with Esther.

Soon the subtleties started.

Grave markers appeared at some new graves without solicitation or explanation. They just were there in place at the head of the grave. Nobody knew how. Most were newly and accurately etched. All apparently came from the surplus Eppie had left behind. Many of these markers decorated the graves of individuals from families who could ill afford to pay for them.

"His ghost had to be doing it," the neighbor speculated. "I know nobody else was. It had to be his ghost. All that big supply of markers he left behind—they were slowly getting gone. They had to be used. That's the way he wanted it, too."

Then the Mortimer family brought Esther back home, not to live, but for her burial in a little country church cemetery not far away.

Soon after the burial, a grave marker appeared at the head of her grave—a native slate marker, flawless in design and engraving, distinctively reflecting Eppie's craftsmanship.

Her parents would have none of it. Esther's father, more irascible than ever, wrestled the marker out of the ground and threw it over the cemetery's rock wall.

Next day it was back in place. Vehemently, old Grant Mortimer forced the marker out of the ground, threw it over the wall, then used a sledgehammer to pound it into little pieces. He had another large granite tombstone cemented into place at the head of his daughter's grave plot.

By and by, two grave markers got together at an unusual location—a quiet glade down by Ribbon Creek, the same spot where two young lovers rendezvoused many years earlier. Wild flowers grew up around the handsome markers which faced each other. The murmuring creek serenaded them, along with the wind in the trees. Breezes whispered their names in a lullaby. The neighbor, who owned the land, wouldn't let Grant Mortimer or anyone else disturb this spot. He called it sacred.

The markers were the same ones he had discovered concealed in Eppie's shop. Now they were newly and accurately engraved. They stood with dignity, almost as if they were ready to embrace each other. The neighbor said that you could look the Uwharries over and find many of Eppie's grave markers, but never one as perfect as these two, saluting each other at Ribbon Creek.

"Eppie may have had angels helping him on those last two," the neighbor said. "You can go there and be quiet and still for a few moments. You feel peace and wholesomeness. You feel fortified and energized with love. You feel like waltzing and dancing and singing. You feel almost like–like–nothing will ever go wrong in your life again. It's powerful. It's spiritual."

Consider it your lucky day if ever you encounter these two special grave markers with the friendly eyes, deep in the Uwharrie woods. Tarry a while. Be quiet, still, and listen. Pay careful attention to those pairs of expressive eyes.

But don't be misled. Those eyes aren't staring at you. They're staring at each other.

THE TREETOP GHOST

Today's scientists might be interested in a report of a ghostly occurrence in the southeastern part of the Uwharries maybe a century ago. Names of the coon hunters who experienced it have never been authenticated, but people have talked about it for generations.

Some called it the ghost of the treetops, a flying gargoyle, a soaring reptile, a holdover from the age of dinosaurs.

Apparently no one knows if it really happened, or if it has re-occurred since the last known report about one hundred years ago.

Three or four Anson County coon hunters, each with a dog or two, set out one cold December night. They planned to stay out all night and train their dogs on this hunt in the hills alongside the Pee Dee River. In the mixture of old and young hounds, the hunters' objective was to give the younger dogs experience in following their elders in tracking down and treeing coons and possums.

Half a century ago, Fet Linder, an old man then, talked about his participation in the legendary hunt.

"We heard the dogs baying up a tree on a hilltop, almost out of hearing. We hurried toward them, yelling to let them know we wuz coming. All uphill. We wuz tired out completely time we got there. Dogs a-going crazy, barking up and jumping up the trunks of them tall trees. Pines and oaks, I think. Our light weren't good enough. Couple of lanterns, couple of old flashlights. Didn't go halfway up toward the top. An' up in the top wuz where the commotion wuz. We could hear it good, but we couldn't see a thing. Black night, no moon, still, no wind a-blowing.

"Something big and heavy was moving around in the tops of them trees. Weren't no possum or coon. Hell no! Sounded like something big and heavy as a plow mule or buggy hoss or a bull. We could hear them limbs creaking and swaying. Some of 'em broke and fell, 'cause we come back and looked later in daylight. Sounded like it wuz struggling to climb up and re-position itself. Sounded like it slipped and hurt itself now and then and sorta mumbled in pain. We were desperate to see what it wuz. But no way. Nobody wanted to try climbing a tree that big. We had an axe with us, but you can't cut down trees that big with one ol' axe. We scattered out all around and looked up from different directions, but too many trees and limbs in the way. Couldn't see nuttin'.

"Then it left. It sprung up outta them treetops and whuffed away like I've never heard before or since. All my buddies were shell-shocked. Me, too. We stood there scared to death, our eyes bulging and our mouths open. You woulda been, too. The dogs even quieted down for a moment, but then they took off again. That thing, big and heavy as it wuz, had to have broad wings, powerful wings, and powerful legs, too, for once it sprung up outta them treetops, its wings took over. We felt 'em. Man, we felt 'em. It musta give two or three downward flaps of them big wings. We felt the pressure all the way to the ground. Felt like a whirlwind. Or a tornado. Stripped off the leaves and some branches from the tree. Flurried up all the dead leaves on the ground. Blowed off our hats. Blowed out the two lanterns. It coulda sucked us up with it, I reckon. We could feel them trees vibrating down the trunks all they way into the ground.

"It screamed, or yelled, as it went up. Never heard any animal go like that. Loud, scary, kinda like a loud crackle of thunder. Maybe like a bunch of rebel yells all put together or a whole tribe of Indian war whoops combined. Didn't sound like it wuz hurt. Kinda like it wuz glad—glad to be free outta them treetops. But it wuz horrible, like a bunch of demons a-yelling. For years we tried to duplicate that yell ourselves, but we couldn't ever come close.

"Well, it whuffed away out of hearing. The dogs took off after it. We found our hats and relit our lanterns. By then the dogs had treed again. Way over on a ridgetop. Musta been a mile away. We could hear 'em good because we wuz on top of a hill, too. Weren't no normal tree barking. Them dogs were crazy barking. We figured that flying monster had landed in the treetops again and the dogs were telling us to come and get 'im. Musta took us half an hour to get there, through all them thickets and up steep hillsides. Tired us out tireder than a day's plowing or newgrounding. Just as we got under them trees, it took off again. All that powerful wing flapping which broke off the leaves and limbs and trembled the whole trunks. Showered us with leaves and snapped out our lanterns. That blast of wind staggered us around and that shrill cry like a madman ten times over just about deafened us.

"Them dogs, they quieted down and whimpered some. They didn't take out after it this time. It whuffed out of hearing and wuz gone. Never heard it again. Nobody else ever did, far as I know. Wish we coulda seen it. Wish it had been daylight instead of midnight. I don't pretend to know what it wuz. Nobody does that we've told this to. Except some people think we're touched in the head and making it up. All I know is that it wuz big and heavy and it could fly through the sky. It could land in treetops, then take off again outta the treetops. I'll never forget them huge whuffing wings that beat down wind on us like a hurricane."

A dinosaur buff likens the above description to a pterosaur, the world's largest flying reptile, which could fly at speeds of twenty-five miles per hour and dip its toothed beak into the surface of a lake to scoop up fish.

But pterosaurs, along with dinosaurs, became extinct sixty-five million years ago.

Or did they?

SNEEZ-ER-ROO

Cicero was the boy who sneezed. Boy, did he sneeze!

Nobody knows where he came from and no one will ever know what happened to him at the end. This mystery of origin and demise perpetuates an ever-growing dimension of ghostliness and bizarre overtones to one of the most enigmatic tales ever to come out of the Uwharries.

His nickname quickly evolved from Cicero to something like "Sis-er-roo," then to "Sneez-er," then to "Sneez-er-roo." Later they settled for plain "Roo." The school kids named him. Most of his contemporaries took full advantage of his unusual, though involuntary, proclivity for sneezing. The kids brought him to the attention of the adults in the community, who maximized his potential. Some people claim this practice of daily overworking Roo is what led to his demise.

The first time it happened, it took the classroom by complete surprise, especially the gray-haired teacher, Miss Nellie. She jerked her spectacles off and furrowed her forehead into what the kids called her "frying pan" frown. Her ruler rapped for order. But nobody, not even Principal Murdock, could have restored order quickly in the room full of pesky kids at old Thickety Creek School—not after an explosion like they had just witnessed.

"Dynamite! It sounded just like dynamite when we blast stumps," shrieked Chevis Kerr, a rangy eighth-grader and one of the two bullies in the room. The other bully was hulky Mason Wiley, who read like a first-grader.

"It shook the building," called Smiley Hect from the back of the room.

"Windows rattled, too," observed Catface Riggins. Catface looked more foxish than cattish. But since Foxface was harder to say, everyone called him Catface. He seldom missed anything. Foxy would be a good name for the inside of him.

All eyes focused near the center of the room on Roo. Flame-haired, freckle-faced Roo looked startled, as if he was as surprised as anyone. His wide eyes and open mouth projected a blank expression as if only a little bit of him was really present, that most of him was off somewhere far away. Sweat plastered a lock of rumpled hair to his forehead. His big ears looked like they would flap when the wind blew. He looked like a winded horse. All loose objects in a five-foot swath in front of Roo's sneeze had been blown to the floor. Student art and papers on one section of the wall flew helter skelter. Some had gone out an open window.

Miss Nellie rapped again. Some of the tumult subsided. The air of expectancy intensified around Roo.

"I just sneezed–I reckon–" he croaked, looking around helplessly, sure that no one believed him.

"Sneeze, my eye!" Mason Wiley roared. "Sounded like the world war."

"I thought a lightning bolt had hit us," squealed one of the girls.

"I coulda swore a tore-naid-oh touched down," hollered Hilburn Lattimore from over near the windows.

"Yeah, yeah," Shriker Peal agreed from the corner. Shriker agreed with just about everything.

The door jerked open and in waddled a short fat man with a glistening bald head. "What happened, Miss Nellie? Anybody hurt or anything?"

"Nobody hurt, Mr. Murdock. Nothing damaged much," Miss Nellie said in her gravelly voice. "We think it must have been Roo–"

Again all eyes swung to Roo. He trembled in his shoes. His heart pounded so hard that the front of his faded shirt quivered. Those nearby felt sorry for him.

"I just sneezed, I reckon," Roo said again.

"That new boy, huh?" Murdock waggled over close to Roo, looking at him intently. "This whole building trembled and vibrated. I saw dust coming out a window. That dangling light in my office jiggled. I heard a few people screaming. Must of thought it was an earthquake or something. You did all that by sneezing?"

"Yessir–I mean, no, sir," Roo stammered. "I mean I don't really know for sure. When I sneeze, I just sorta go blank with my eyes closed and all. I can't really tell what happens. But I don't want to cause no trouble to anybody."

Murdock robotted around back to Miss Nellie's desk. "Better keep a closer eye on that bird," he whispered. "If he keeps this up, we'll have to take some action."

The class surveyed the damage and began straightening up.

Burp Langston, who sat in the desk behind him, put his hand on Roo's shoulder. "Don't let them scare you so much, Roo. Nobody can help sneezing."

Roo's friendly eyes looked up puppy-like. "Yeah, I know, but–it's like something gets hold of me–I freeze, like a spasm–I don't know when–I can't stop it!"

Ten minutes later Catface asked to be excused. He was gone just long enough to reach the boys' bathroom, and then he was back. He detoured by Roo's desk, pausing just an instant. His hand made a quick movement toward Roo's face. Those nearby smelled the sweet, sickly odor of powdered snuff. Catface hurried on to his seat. Miss Nellie tried to explain a math problem.

Only seconds passed. Roo's shoulders hunched upward for a moment. Then again. He sucked in air fiercely. He was winding up to sneeze again. His body trembled. His hands gripped his desk. He sucked in enough air to explode. Like dynamite!

"Look out!" Burp Langston yelled. "Roo's gonna sneeze again. Get down under your desks. Hurry!"

Every kid scrambled out of his desk and hunkered down beside it. Miss Nellie shoved her chair backward and crawled under her desk like a frightened puppy. Some kids squealed and eeked. Most just watched in fascination.

Roo half rose, body rigid, hands deadlocked on his desk edges to anchor himself. His body rocked and his head bobbed. Then his body appeared to explode in a fearsome roar. The main force of his explosion slapped another section of the inside wall, causing a rattle, a crash, and a jangle of broken glass.

Exhausted, Roo sank limply back into his seat.

More humbly this time, they surveyed the damage. Books littered the floor. More papers had blown off the wall, along with chalk and erasers. One end of a piece of blackboard molding had ripped loose.

And George Washington had tumbled down from his perch on the wall. With his frame knocked askew and his glass shattered, George looked out pensively while impaled on the corner post of Miss Nellie's desk chair.

"Shazam!" Mason Wiley said reverently for everyone.

"And uh-zam, zam, zam!" echoed Shriker Peal.

The room door banged open and in waddled Murdock, with his bald head and round face both red, and his mouth sputtering.

"Did that boy sneeze again?" Miss Nellie nodded. "Anybody hurt this time?" She shook her head. He looked at George Washington impaled on the chair post. His face grew redder.

He jerked around until he spotted Roo. "You, come with me to my office. I want to talk to you." He beckoned with a fat finger.

Like a frightened, big-eyed rabbit, Roo rose to comply. He looked like a man walking to the gallows.

Burp Langston rose. "Mr. Murdock, I'm his best friend. Let me come with you. Please?"

Murdock glared. He nodded, then jerked his head toward the door.

Burp negotiated lighter punishment for Roo. They decided to assign Roo to the thick-walled boiler room and let ol' Mister Pexman, the janitor, read a story to him now and then. One day when the coal dust overcame him, Roo sneezed into the open door of the boiler firebox. It dowsed the fire and sent such a blast of air through the pipe system that all the radiators in the building jiggled and danced.

While Roo stayed in the boiler room, Burp served as his liaison between his classmates and Murdock. But school faded. Murdock was happy to see Roo leave. Catface and the others told everyone about Roo's special gift. And everyone wanted to see it demonstrated.

In spite of Burp's objections, Catface and Chevis worked out an arsenal of potent stimulants to make Roo sneeze. Using these "triggers" for control, they tried to rent Roo out for various practical applications in the community, some of which succeeded. Then the adults ignored the boys and commandeered Roo as a community resource, using him for purposes practical and frivolous. Every day someone had Roo, using and abusing him.

Burp tried hard to prevent this criminal brutality of his friend. But he could not become a full-time guardian and accompany Roo on every trip. No adult would listen to his pleas for moderation. Most people found Roo's gift so tantalizingly exotic, they wanted maximum utilization, though most of it was motivated by curiosity.

Meantime, on the rare instances when no one molested Roo, Burp learned more about his friend.

Always in the early morning, Roo appeared on the east side of Crowder's Ridge, walking toward the settlement. Nobody knew where he came from. He just appeared there.

"Where do you live?" Burp asked.

"I stay on the other side of the ridge," Roo answered.

Burp knew nobody lived on the west side of Crowder's Ridge. It was too steep. Nothing there but wilderness—ravines, boulders, trees, thickets, and roaming bobcats.

"Do you have a pappy and mammy? Brothers and sisters?" Burp asked. Roo shook his head. "Where were you before you came here?"

Roo glanced at the sky. "Far, far away," he said.

"Will you be going back there?" Roo nodded. "Where you come from, does everybody there sneeze like you do?" Roo just laughed. "No home, no family, what do you do all night?"

"I look at the stars," Roo said. "I like the stars, especially shooting stars."

Burp joined him some nights in a clearing on the east side of Crowder's Ridge, and they watched the stars. Roo usually knew just where to look. He seldom missed a meteor. Burp saw more shooting stars than he had ever seen before. At times he felt like he and Roo were up there among the shooting stars, maybe astraddle one and guiding it through the heavens.

Early each morning a line of fans and manipulators formed on the flank of Crowder's Ridge to greet Roo and hustle him off to do their bidding. Many days he performed at a dozen or so locations before they brought him back, exhausted, at day's end and dumped him out on the same spot. But always next morning he appeared rejuvenated and ready.

Many of the exploits were memorable and creative.

Usually two strong men held Roo horizontally like a log and pointed his face at the target. Slide a stimulant, like red hot pepper, under his nose and he roared off like a cannon.

Blindley Mox used Roo to defoliate his cotton patch prior to picking time.

Asap Lowingbriar borrowed Roo to blow his roosting guineas from the top of a tree. He also used Roo to dislodge roosting chickens from the inner ramparts of the barn, although this partially backfired because the sneeze blew off some of the metal roofing.

Another man harnessed Roo's sneezing to power his bateau and raft up the river and across the lake. He said it worked lots better than paddling.

Enterprising farmers used Roo to help clean out their chicken houses in preparation for a new brood. A few sneezes blasted out all the dust, spider webs, droppings, and floor litter.

A bird hunter synchronized Roo sneezes to bring down almost an entire covey of quail after his pointer dog flushed them. Duck and geese hunters used the same method.

Nuts and grapes high in trees turned loose and showered down once Roo's sneeze focused on them.

Another farmer used Roo to scatter powdered insecticide and herbicide over his fields.

An entrepreneur rigged up a big sail atop a four-wheeled wagon, and used Roo's sneezes to propel him around country roads and fields.

They used Roo to unclog chimneys, blow the snow off roofs, and, when the wind died, to turn the windmill blades to pump water.

When water in the mill race ran low, they made Roo sneeze into the empty buckets of the big waterwheel to turn it and grind corn.

Practically every household used him to blow dead leaves out of the yard.

Forest fires were stopped in their tracks when Roo loosed a few sneezes on them.

Fishermen took Roo out to the middle of the river and made him sneeze back toward the shore. It created a huge wall of water, which slammed over the bank, depositing fish everywhere.

Happy Hobberhart took Roo to the open door of a country church one Sunday morning, and made him sneeze into a large pan filled with moonshine, which sprinkled over the entire congregation and choir. Hats, songbooks, Bibles, fans, and handbags sailed through the air. The preacher cowered behind the pulpit. Glass panes popped out of windows. A large wooden cross, suspended from the ceiling, rocked to and fro like a pendulum. Staggering and guffawing, Happy grabbed Roo and hightailed it back to his old Ford and chick-a-lacked away before the men of the congregation boiled outside to intercept him.

When they could sneak him away, Catface and the other boys used Roo to knock over haystacks, explode shocks of dying grain, scatter drying clothes off the clothesline, send clouds of dust into crowds of people, and to hike up the dress tails of females.

Lonzo Bassy used Roo to spray paint his barn. He carefully positioned a large container of paint and made Roo get behind it and sneeze toward the barn. One sneeze spattered paint over one whole side.

Superstitious people who had never seen Roo sneeze would not believe that such bedlam was caused by one man sneezing. They attributed it to ghosts and evil spirits.

After a year or two of such sneezannigans, Roo began to wilt. He turned pale, thinner, wheezed a little, had sunken eyes and that emaciated appearance. His eyes begged for relief. Burp felt so sorry for Roo that he wanted to cry. He pleaded with everyone to lay off and give Roo time to recuperate. But nobody did. They continued to use and abuse him.

They noticed a slowdown in his sneezes. Less frequent. A little weaker. Stimulants didn't work as well. It took him longer to build up air pressure for a ferocious sneeze. Unattended when he sneezed, his feet almost lifted off the ground as if he were blasting himself into space.

"You want me to go with you to see old Doctor Hansey and let him check you over and give you some medicine to pep you up?" Burp asked one evening while they relaxed and watched stars.

"No," Roo responded. "I'm just a little tired, but I'll be okay. Anyway, I won't be here much longer."

"Where are you going?"

"Back," Roo said. That's all he ever said about his destination.

"Take me with you. Please," Burp pleaded.

Roo looked at his friend for a long time, then finally shook his head.

A few days later the early morning crowd waiting for Roo to appear had a longer wait. They waited all day. Then all day the next day and the next. Burp tried to tell them waiting was useless, but no one believed him.

After a week they decided to search out Crowder's Ridge, particularly the west side. There they found no human life or sign of human habitation. Gradually they grew convinced that Roo was gone, permanently, though no one knew how or where. He became an instant legend, replete with intense speculation and tall tales, all with ghostly overtones. Those with firsthand knowledge competed to see who could relate the weirdest experience.

Everyone associated Roo with shooting stars. Would he ever come back? Were there others like him up there?

Sometimes, in the presence of newcomers, they would tell each other dramatically, "If a shooting star lands in your yard and dumps out a tow-headed, freckle-faced, big-eared boy, you may have another Sneez-er-roo on your hands."

Burp never left the community and he lived to be an old man. As a young adult, he bought a piece of land and built a modest home in the clearing on the east flank of Crowder's Ridge. It became an ideal place to watch the stars, for which Burp developed a passion. In his last years, he sat outside and stargazed for half the night. When a shooting star punctuated the heavens, he smiled, raised his arm, and waved as if greeting a friend.